DIMOND OF ALASKA

Adventurer in the Far North

DIMOND
OF ALASKA

Adventurer in the Far North

BY EDWARD A. HERRON

ᐱᐱᐱᐱᐱᐱᐱᐱᐱᐱᐱᐱ

KINGSTON HOUSE · CHICAGO

Published Originally by Julian Messner, Inc.
New York

Published simultaneously in Canada
by The Copp Clark Publishing Co. Limited

Printed in the United States of America
Library of Congress Catalog Card No. 57-11501

TO

LAURA ORDWAY

AN ALASKAN

DIMOND OF ALASKA

Adventurer in the Far North

CHAPTER ONE

The young man closed the door gently behind him.

He hesitated a moment, then placed his traveling bag firmly on the wooden flooring of the porch.

"Can't just leave Uncle Dan without saying anything," he muttered.

He reached into his pocket for a pencil and a slip of paper. For a moment he looked thoughtfully at the red ball of sun dropping behind the tree-lined Mohawk River. No need to write a long letter as he had done to his mother and father who lived across the river on the farm at Palatine Bridge. He wrote three words boldly and stuffed the note into the mail slot. He whispered a short prayer, then reached for his bag, and without another backward glance walked briskly from the town of Canojoharie in New York.

Behind him the message fluttered in the evening breeze.

Tony Dimond was twenty-two years old, tall and lean. He kept his head lifted to the darkening sky. In his long, swinging stride there was a great determination, a forward surge that almost brought him to a half-trot. Only once did he stop, beating a quick tattoo across his waist. His fingers reached into his coat, and fingered the new money belt. He nodded in satisfaction, and kept going down the dusty road.

It was seven o'clock in the evening in the spring of 1904.

There was a clopping sound of hooves striking the dirt, the protesting rasp of wheels digging wider ruts in the road.

"Evening, teacher!"

Tony spun about. He lifted his free hand in greeting to the farmer perched on the wagon seat. "Good evening, Mr. Snyder."

"Heading somewhere, Tony? Give you a lift?"

"I'm taking the local train over to Utica. Then I'm catching the Limited for Chicago."

"Chi—Chicago? Hey," Mr. Snyder said as Tony swung up beside him, "won't you be a mite late getting back to teach school?"

"I'm not coming back. Didn't Rufus tell you?"

"Tell me what? That boy—I'm lucky he tells me the time of the day. Never saw such a one for getting his nose down into a book and just reading and reading—and—wait a minute," Mr. Snyder broke off abruptly. "What didn't Rufus tell me? Where you going?"

"I'm going to Alaska. I've resigned as the school teacher. I'm not coming back."

"Whoa, Jamie. Whoa, slow down, boy." Mr. Snyder pulled back on the reins. "You feeling all right, son?" He looked at Tony critically, sniffing slightly, his nose wrinkling like a rabbit. "You're not a drinking man, Tony?"

"Never had a drop in my life, Mr. Snyder. And I never felt better. I tell you, I'm going to Alaska! I thought everybody in town knew about it! Why, I've just been waiting until a new teacher could be found to take my place. Look—here's my Pullman ticket, my steamship ticket. It's real—I'm going!"

Mr. Snyder clucked to the horse. He kept his head averted from Tony, but his eyes rolled in circles to cover the new suit, the gleaming shoes, and the bulging traveling bag.

"You're going some place, that's sure," Mr. Snyder muttered. He kept talking to himself in half-whispers, rolling his eyes sideways from time to time to get a closer look at the young man sitting erect on the seat beside him. "How far is it to that there place, Alaska?"

"Four thousand miles, maybe a little more. That is, to Valdez, where I'm heading."

Mr. Snyder said nothing. He kept his head pointed rigidly forward. "Uncle of mine," he finally volunteered, "went to the Klondike in '98. Never did hear from him again. Froze to death maybe."

Tony wasn't paying attention. He kept looking down the road. Plenty of time to catch the train. It wasn't due until nine o'clock. Meet the new teacher, George Bender, at the brief midnight stop in Utica and tell him what to expect at the school. Then just sit there in the train and head west to Chicago, Seattle—Alaska.

"Tony, why don't you stay with teaching? A young man with your talents, your education—you should keep on teaching. New York State needs men like you. There's no telling what the future could hold. The ten dollars a week you're making now is only a start."

Tony shook his head firmly. He wouldn't listen. It wasn't teaching he wanted. He kept thinking of the letters he had received from his old schoolmate, Joe Murray, telling of the most thrilling land of all—Alaska! He lifted his head again. "What is it, sir? What is it you were saying?"

"I said, who's going to be the new schoolteacher? Ain't just going off and leave us with no schoolteacher, are you? You're not the kind of a man who'd. . . ."

"I guess you didn't hear me, Mr. Snyder. That's all taken care of. There's a young fellow coming over from Utica—George Harvey Bender. He's volunteered to finish out the school term in my place."

Mr. Snyder didn't say any more. He kept repeating the word "Alaska" under his breath. Occasionally he interlaced the words, "darn fools," and always he kept shaking his head. Suddenly he cupped his wire-haired chin in one hand, and looked sideways at Tony. "That boy, Rufus, that son of mine. Caught him reading a book last night, *Call of the Wild*. Written by a fellow name Jack Paris or Jack London. That a story about the Maine woods?"

"No, sir, it isn't. It's about the Yukon. It's one of the finest stories ever written about the North. I loaned it to Rufus. When he finishes it, he'll be as much in love with Alaska as I am."

"Drat nab it, Dimond, it's just what I thought. You've poisoned that boy's mind. You got him thinking crazy ideas about foreign countries. First thing you know he'll be putting himself in fancy clothes like you and taking off—if I don't stop him."

Snyder pulled back on the reins vigorously. "Whoa,

there, Jamie! Pull up, boy!" The wagon wrenched to a stop. "I'll thank you, Mr. Dimond, to get down off this wagon. I got things to do."

Tony was bewildered. He climbed down and stood in the road. "What is it, Mr. Snyder? Something I've said? Something I've done?"

"You just bet your sweet life it's something you've done, young fellow." Mr. Snyder tossed the bag into the dust and swung the horse about in a wide circle. "I'm going back to my farm and get that book," he yelled over his shoulder, "and I'm going to throw it down the well. Ain't no harebrained book writer or foolish school-teacher going to get my son to run off to a foreign country, they ain't."

The wagon teetered wildly, then straightened and rolled swiftly down the road.

Tony stood with his fist clenched, fighting back his anger. It was that way so often—people not understanding the deep stirring inside, the call for adventure.

He set his jaw determinedly, lifted the heavy bag and started walking. "Must think I'm weak-minded," he muttered. "Keep telling me I'm throwing away so many opportunities right here in Montgomery County." For months he had been hearing the whispered voices. "Somebody ought to put some sense into that young man's head. Stubborn, that's what he is. Following Joe Murray to Alaska. Might just as well go to China."

The road into Amsterdam seemed to go on forever. No wagons passed to offer him a lift. Tony was conscious of his new shoes. They seemed to come alive and develop little teeth that nibbled at sore spots on his heels. The heavy bag kept knocking against his knees. It seemed to grow heavier, pulling him to one side so that a stitch began to ache between his ribs. The fine new suit that he had bought in preparation for the long journey was suddenly tight and oppressive.

He stopped in the middle of the road, put down the bag, and took off his coat. He looked at the evening stars beginning to show against the sunset. "I've walked only two miles," he thought, "and I'm exhausted. What'll I do when I'm on the trail in Alaska? Maybe I can take exercises on the boat. Maybe. . . ."

There was a noisy chugging behind him, and he spun about. Coming down the road, surrounded by a din of noise, was an automobile. The driver waved grandly, then slowed, and pulled back on the brake. "Going to Amsterdam, son? Can I give you a lift?"

Tony was tempted to shake his head and walk on, but he stopped himself. If I'm going to Alaska, I've got to get used to everything, he thought. He picked up his bag and approached the automobile warily. He tossed his leg over the side and climbed in, sitting rigidly by the driver. The brake was released and the car lurched forward. Tony heard the churning, roaring noise from the big long motor. He saw the roadside trees speed by at a dizzy pace. Chickens squawked and headed for safety as the car roared along.

Tony held firmly to the dashboard with one hand, and clutched his hat with the other. The driver, masked behind thick goggles, looked ahead with all the intensity of a locomotive engineer, his attention riveted on the dim yellow road that flowed beneath them like a dark river.

Suddenly the driver leaned over and shouted into

Tony's ear. "Hold on to your hat, son. I'm going to open her up to thirty miles an hour! Watch her go!"

Tony paled. He forgot his hat and clutched the dashboard with both hands. He lowered his head as though fighting the dizzy speed, shut his eyes, and gritted his teeth. I won't ever live to reach Alaska, he thought wildly. The massive motor roared into a new high pitch. The wheels spun, and the road flew by. The wind lifted Tony's new hat and ripped it from his head. He didn't care. He was concerned only with surviving this new ordeal.

Finally the motor dropped to a softer tone, and the car slowed. The driver, grinning triumphantly, turned to Tony, "What do you think, boy? Some baby, eh?"

"Please let me out. I don't feel well."

The driver looked hurt. He stopped the car and helped Tony gently to the ground. "What's the matter? You never ridden in a car before?"

"No. Never. Saw them, but never rode in them. Guess I just—too much excitement." He put his bag by the side of the road and sat down on it. The driver shook his head and pulled away into the night. Tony didn't even watch him go. He thought of his new hat, lying in the dust a half mile back. "I don't care," he whispered. He picked up his bag and started limping along the road to Amsterdam.

Number 167, the local for Utica, blared a warning whistle, and came to a stop at the small station. Tony pulled himself painfully aboard. He was deeply discouraged, and his feet hurt. He wished he had bought some sensible clothing, instead of these that made him look like a dude. Mostly he wished he had prepared for the trip by getting into good physical condition. "I've only come five miles," he thought, "and I feel awful." He tried to sit upright for the two-hour train ride over to Utica but the pain beneath his ribs was terrific. He kept rubbing his hand tenderly over his side. He sat stiffly on the coarse green cushions, lonely and uncertain. Maybe it was foolish, giving up a teaching career just to search for adventure in a distant land. Perhaps he should have been sensible, like his Uncle Dan McEwen had said, and stayed at home.

"EXTRA, EXTRA! READ ALL ABOUT IT!"

A news butcher came through the train waving a paper, and mouthing a long string of unintelligible words. Tony stopped him. "Let me have a paper," he said.

When he read the words, the old excitement began to storm down on him. "New Gold Strike in Alaska! Thousand prospectors start over the Copper River trail to stake claims in new mining district. Million dollar bonanza."

"I'm going," Tony whispered as he read the story over and over. "I'm going. Nothing will stop me!"

Suddenly he was ravenously hungry. He looked about, waiting impatiently for the return of the news butcher who would be hawking sandwiches and milk. In the excitement of leaving, Tony had been unable to eat. He remembered dimly a noon hour that had sped by in bashful good-bys from the line of pupils waiting outside the classroom door. And breakfast had been overlooked in that hurried rush of packing in the early morning hours.

"Wait a minute," he told himself, smiling in the darkness. "Meals won't come easily in Alaska. You'll have to work for your dinner—shoot a bear, a moose or a deer." He began to picture himself swinging along the trail, rifle ready, primed for any savory game that might chance across his path. But suddenly the bear and the deer and the moose were lost in thick slabs of bread and jam, and in vast heaps of mashed potatoes and gravy.

He began to think of meals he had enjoyed. His concentration was so great, and his hunger so tormenting that the money belt strapped inside his coat began to cut deeply into his skin. He looked cautiously about the darkened car, listening to the faint snores and heavy breathing from the other passengers. Then quietly he unfastened the money belt. He slipped it inside the traveling bag nestled by his feet. For just a moment he fingered proudly the identification tag:

Anthony J. Dimond,
Care of PHOENIX HOTEL,
Valdez, Alaska

The hotel would be his jumping-off place. He would buy his outfit in Valdez: a gold pan, pick and shovel, an ample supply of grub, rifle and ammunition—what more did a man need before plunging into the heart of Alaska?

But he was still hungry.

He looked about anxiously, wondering if a man might possibly starve to death while crossing New York State on a train. He tried to remember the magazine stories he had read of survival in the wilderness, and the hunger in his stomach overrode all else.

He could think of only one thing—food.

When the train churned noisily into the station at Utica he leaped to his feet and almost ran down the aisle to lose no time. The restaurant in the station would be open. Perhaps he could talk to George Bender while he was eating. The Limited would be along in less than twenty minutes. It would be a close connection, but if everything went all right. . . .

He walked hurriedly along the platform, scanning the faces that appeared under the yellow electric lights. Bender was nowhere in sight. He went into the waiting room, eyeing each person who sat on the hard, uncomfortable seats. There was a delightful smell of sizzling meat from the small lunch counter at one end of the station. For one moment he was tempted to eat first, and look for George afterwards. But he put it out of his mind. Time was flying.

There was a young man in immaculately tailored clothes and brilliant yellow shoes who stood off to one side, almost as though he were a census taker, counting the number of prospective passengers in the waiting room. He was short, broad, and plump. He lifted one finger and touched it delicately to the thin mustache above his lip.

Tony eyed the young man with a tinge of disappointment. Then he approached, nodded and thrust out his hand. "You're George Bender?"

"That is right. And you must be Mister Anthony Dimond." He rolled the name off as though he were a train announcer calling a departure.

"Glad to see you," Tony said explosively. "I've only twenty minutes between trains, and I want to tell you all about the Marshville school, and the pupils you'll be teaching, and all. . . ."

"Mister Dimond. . . ."

"What is it, George, I mean, Mr. Bender? Nothing wrong, is there?" Tony half-turned and looked back longingly toward the lunch counter. "Could we sit down and eat a sandwich while we talk? I'm starving. . . ."

George Bender shook his head. He put down his bag and squared his feet. "Guess you're not the only one that's searching for adventure, Tony. Ever since I first heard from you, asking me to come over and take your place at the school, I've been reading about Alaska." He tugged at his mustache nervously. "Don't know just how to tell you, Tony—but I'm not going to be a school-teacher, either—I'm heading north to Alaska."

Tony stared at him in disbelief. "You mean—this coming summer? Next year?"

George Bender shook his head. He leaned over and picked up his suitcase. "I mean right now. I'm catching the Limited to Chicago in exactly five minutes. Maybe we'll be riding together.

Tony swayed slightly. He rubbed his hand nervously. Then he straightened up and held out his hand. "Good luck, George."

"Aren't you coming with me?"

"Sorry, no. We can't leave that school without a teacher. I'll have to go back. Maybe someday," he added almost wistfully as he turned away, "we'll meet in Alaska."

He stood on the platform, watching the red lights of the Limited blink and disappear as the train picked up speed and vanished toward Syracuse, Buffalo, Cleveland

and Chicago. His train was going, and he was not on it. The ship in Seattle would be leaving, and he would not be aboard. All the dreams and longings of the past three years were disappearing with the train that rounded a curve and vanished into the night.

It was then he realized for the first time that his traveling bag, with all his money in the leather belt, was missing. In his hurry, he had leaped from the train and left it behind.

Not only were his dreams of Alaska shattered, but he was almost penniless.

He had ninety-eight cents left in his pockets. For forty-five cents, he bought the best dinner available at the lunch counter. Then, with the remaining fifty-three cents jingling in his pocket he started walking.

He was forty-one miles from home. And he had his back turned on Alaska. The dream of adventure was gone.

He walked through the night without stopping. The sun was beginning to climb above the treetops as he passed through the sleeping town of St. Johnsville.

Tony's head was swimming with fatigue when he approached a farm beyond Palatine Bridge. A tall, gray-haired farmer, his face seamed and weather-beaten, looked up as Tony turned into the lane. He left the horses he was following and walked over with his hand extended. "Trouble?" he asked.

"Yes, Dad. Real trouble." Tony blurted out the story of the night's disappointment.

John Dimond listened sympathetically, "Get aboard Kaydee, there," he said, indicating one of the horses, "and we'll ride up to the house for some of your mother's pancakes."

Tony vaulted easily onto the back of the big brown horse and nudged him gently. As the horse moved along, Tony looked far over the wide, rolling acres of the farm. It was here he had been born, here he had spent a happy childhood with his three brothers and two sisters. All of his young life he had ridden in these fields, the horses galloping with lumbering speed to the barn when the day's chores had been finished. Tony had gone coon hunting in the nearby woodlands. With his younger brothers tagging behind, he had explored the little creeks that wandered through the countryside before joining the Mohawk River.

From this pleasant farm he had gone into the Mohawk Valley six years ago, to teach the district schools at Marshville, Wagner's Hollow, and Nose Hill before his present assignment at Canojoharie.

"Had a letter from Herbert," his father said. "He wants to thank you for sending his tuition money at school."

Tony nodded in reply. In the Dimond family, it was traditional that the older children help the younger ones to attain a coveted high school education with the nuns at Saint Mary's Catholic Institute in Amsterdam. He shaded his eyes and looked at the old farmhouse with its high ridge where he and his cousin Anna once had walked in an amateur balancing act that had horrified his parents.

His mother was standing on the porch. She held out her arms to her teacher-son. "Don't say anything now, Anthony," she said. "Just you come and sit down to breakfast with your father."

He ate quietly, his eyes lifted to the book shelves that overflowed even into the kitchen of the Dimond house. A complete set of Dickens was arranged like a row of soldiers above the big flour barrel. Emma Dimond, well educated for her time, pulled a book from her apron pocket and slipped it back on the shelf. "Manley's returned it," she explained. "Wants us to send Janie over with *Oliver Twist* next week."

Finally Tony finished eating the huge breakfast. When his mother had listened to his story of the night's happenings, she nodded slowly. "Anthony, you must not be discouraged. At your age there is a great deal of adventure still waiting. Thank the dear Lord that you have good health and a good education. Everything else will come."

His father, who was sixty-four years old, was trembling slightly, a reminder of the malaria that had plagued him constantly since his Civil War service. He placed his arm about Tony's shoulder. "I'm glad you did not forget your duty to the school, Anthony. Alaska's a big country. It's not going to run away. It will still be waiting. Come along. I'll hitch up the wagon and take you to your Uncle's in Canojoharie so you'll not be late for school."

When Tony finally reached Uncle Dan McEwen's home which he had left so confidently the night before, he said good-by to his father and walked up the path to the silent house where he boarded. The note was still fluttering in the mailbox. He read it once more.

"Gone to Alaska. Tony Dimond."

He tore the note into little pieces and went inside.

CHAPTER TWO

ΛΛΛΛΛΛΛΛΛΛΛΛΛΛΛΛΛΛΛΛΛΛΛΛΛΛΛΛΛΛ

"Teacher's back!"
"He didn't go to Alaska!"
"My Dad says. . . ."
Tony heard the whispers of the pupils as he strode up the steps of the Marshville schoolhouse. His face was grim. He didn't look to the right or left. When he went into the schoolroom he waited with his back turned, looking out of the window, until the room had filled. Then he turned about. The talking stopped. He saw Rufus Snyder, a quiet, thoughtful-eyed boy of sixteen, staring fixedly at him.

"You're surprised to see me," Tony said. "I'm surprised to be here." He brushed the dust that still clung to his clothing from the nightlong walk. "I thought I'd be in Chicago at this moment, waiting for the train to take me to Seattle. I couldn't get a substitute teacher, so I came back." He lifted his eyes and fixed them on Rufus Snyder. "We can't always do what we want to. Sometimes we must think of others."

Rufus Snyder rose to his feet. "Will you be leaving soon—when another teacher gets here?"

Tony felt the three pennies in his pocket. He hesitated. "I don't know." He looked at the clock. "Open your arithmetic books, please. We're behind schedule."

"Mr. Dimond?"

"Yes, Rufus?"

"Can't we start with geography? Won't you tell us about Alaska again?"

Despite the weariness that overwhelmed him, Tony grinned. "It's an old trick, Rufe. You know very well if I get started on Alaska, I'll keep going until ten o'clock— right past arithmetic time."

"Please, Mr. Dimond."

Tony didn't need any urging. His eyes gleamed as he rolled down the big map of the Northland. It spread the entire length of the blackboard. The map was one he had bought from the Government Printing Office in Washington, D. C. He forgot the blisters on his heels, the biting pain in his side. The weight of weariness from the sleepless night slipped away from him as he began to talk.

He swept his hand across the slick paper, touching lightly on the thousand green islands of the Inside Passage, the wide waters of the Gulf of Alaska, the long dagger sweep of the Aleutian Islands, and the vast empty spaces marking the tundra of the Interior. "Over here," he said, "is Dawson in Yukon Territory, where they had the first big gold stampede six years ago, in 1898. Way up in this corner is Nome, where they started mining on the beaches in '99. And here is Fairbanks, right in the very center, where they had that big gold strike just two years ago."

He stood back and looked at the map. "It's big," he said, "big as Texas and California and Montana all put together. If a man started in Ketchikan, here in the south, and kept going right out the entire length of the Aleutian Islands, it would be the same as if this class walked from here right to San Francisco." He winced, thinking of his experience the night before.

He smacked the map smartly with the flat of his hand. "There are hundreds and thousands of square miles," he continued excitedly, "where no man has ever been. There's gold, millions and millions of ounces of gold, waiting to be dug, there are fur-bearing animals waiting to be caught, space for a man to live in, to grow in."

He stopped abruptly and rolled up the map. "Arithmetic books, please."

He managed to keep awake through the balance of the day, giving the forty-five pupils in the one-room schoolhouse written assignments, while he paced back and forth, trying to keep his eyes from closing. Then he went home and slept for sixteen hours. He wrote to the New York Central Railroad asking that his traveling bag he traced and returned to him if possible. But he never expected to see it again.

He had saved three years for the six hundred and seventy dollars that was in the money belt. "I can't wait another three years," Tony whispered to himself. "I just can't!" He was grateful when the railroad and the steamship company refunded one hundred and forty dollars for his unused tickets. He knew it was a start toward the money he needed. He still had a long way to go.

Tony had always lived frugally. Now he redoubled his efforts to save, trying to add dollars, half dollars, even quarters to his small account. But he knew there was something even more important than money.

One night when everyone in his uncle's house had fallen asleep, he let himself quietly out the front door, closing it gently behind him. He carried a roll of blankets under his arm. He went through the fields toward the banks of the Mohawk River. In a secluded spot, surrounded by a clump of budding sycamore trees, he spread the blankets and stretched out. "If I'm going to get ready," he said to himself, "I've got to start now."

He could hear the waters of the river gurgling scarcely fifty feet away. He watched the moon rise above the trees, breaking a pathway through a mountain of white clouds. He heard faint noises, and he sat upright, staring around uneasily. Then he heard the faint voices of drivers urging the horses along the path bordering the Erie Canal, shouting to redouble their efforts while they pulled the heavy barges along.

He rolled tight in his blankets. "Before the end of the year," he mused, "I'll be sleeping by the Copper River. I'll have a rifle alongside of me, a gold pan, dogs." He hesitated, remembering the small amount in his savings account. "I'll be lucky if I have a good pair of shoes." The ground was hard, unyielding. He twisted and turned, wondering if he had been foolish to leave the comfort of his soft bed. Finally he fell asleep.

In his dreams he tried to cross a swollen mountain torrent. He slipped and plunged headlong under the water. He woke with a start. Rain was falling in hard, driving gusts. The blankets were soaked through. Worse, he had left his shoes in the open, and they were fast filling with water.

He was shivering violently. Teeth chattering, hands shaking, he slipped on his shoes, grimacing at the queasy feeling. He rolled up the sodden blankets and trudged back to the house in the darkness. He sneezed. "I'm the world's worst explorer," he thought as he crept inside the house. "I'll be lucky if I don't get pneumonia my first night in Alaska!"

But he was determined to be in excellent physical condition for the trip. From that night on he slept outside whenever possible. He began to train with all the intensity of a fighter getting ready for an important match.

One Friday evening, when the school week was finished, he left quietly on a two-day camping trip. He made his first attempts at cooking over an open fire. He gashed his finger opening a can of beans. His hunter's stew was thin and watery with a suspiciously flat taste. The sourdough biscuits which he prepared carefully, following a recipe in a magazine article by Jack London, tasted like white glue. When he searched for the six eggs he had brought along, he found that because of improper packing four had broken and dripped down through his blanket roll. But the two remaining eggs he brought to a perfect boil. When he cracked the shells, his right hand reached out instinctively. Then he remembered that he had forgotten to bring salt along.

"Make my mistakes here," he said, trying to force a smile as he chewed methodically on the saltless eggs, "then I won't make them in Alaska."

He never repeated the same mistake. He learned rapidly. Within a short time he could build a fire and prepare a substantial meal with little effort. He sought out the right spots to spread his blankets at night, scooping a hole for his hip, taking advantage of any natural cushioning that might be available.

On week ends he began to explore the roads in Montgomery County. His trips took him farther and farther afield. He developed a long, swinging stride, pretending that he was walking the Abercrombie Trail over the Valdez Glacier. He learned how to conserve his strength, how to make a bed of pine boughs before rolling up his blankets for the night. And he kept his eyes to the sky, learning how to outwit the elements when rain threatened.

As the weeks went by, his muscles began to harden. He rose early each morning to run like a prize fighter around the country roads. On week ends he hiked twenty, thirty miles, deliberately inviting the pangs of hunger. He avoided the traveled highways and struck out across the fields and mountains, seeking the trails of the Indians who once had crisscrossed the green forests of the Mohawk Valley.

Occasionally Rufus Snyder walked home with Tony after the closing of school on Friday afternoons, watching his methodical preparations for another week end in the open. "If I ask my Dad," he said suddenly, "will you let me come with you?"

"No one I'd like more, Rufe. But don't get your hopes up. Your Dad doesn't think I'm the best example in the world for boys, you know."

"You're wrong, Mr. Dimond. He likes you. He really does. Why, he even read the book of Jack London's!"

Tony smiled, remembering the night that Snyder had almost tossed him from the wagon.

"I hope you're right, Rufe." But he said no more.

A sudden epidemic of chicken pox swept through the school, and an unexpected week's holiday was declared. Tony raced home, gathered his gear, and swung off down the open road. Someone was waiting by the gate as he neared the Snyder farm.

"Rufe!" He looked in astonishment at the pack on the boy's back, almost identical with his own. "Where are you going?"

"With you."

Tony shook his head. "I'm sorry, Rufe. I couldn't let you do that. Your Dad would. . . ."

A burly figure straightened from the rows of tall asparagus gone to seed. Mr. Snyder walked to the gate and held out his hand to Tony. "The boy's right, Mr. Dimond. He has my permission—if you'll let him go along."

"We'll be away a full week, Mr. Snyder."

"That's all right with me. We've got the seed in, and I can do without Rufe's help for that time." He hesitated. "I want to tell you how sorry I am about that night, the wagon, getting angry— This is my way of saying I think you're the kind of a man I want my boy to know—Alaska and all!"

He shook hands with Tony, patted Rufe on the back, and turned away hurriedly.

"Come along, Rufe! We're on our way!"

The two swung aboard a train. That night they camped on the shore of Lake George, nearly one hundred miles to the north. In four strenuous days they explored the west shore of the lake.

Tony apologized as he busied himself pouring the flapjack batter into the small frying pan he held over the fire. "I'm afraid I pushed you a little hard today, Rufe. We should have remained a day at Silver Bay and come on up in easy stages. Give those blisters a chance to harden." He nibbled thoughtfully on a flapjack. "Come and get it, Rufe."

There was no answer.

He walked closer to the boy who was sitting on the ground with his back resting against a pine tree. "Rufe? Rufe?"

Rufus Snyder was fast asleep. Tony chuckled and covered the boy with a blanket. Then he went back to the flapjacks.

They explored the green forests that swept down to the lakeside. Tony pointed out all the historical points of interest, trying to bring to life the armies who had fought in this wilderness.

"One of my ancestors, General John Sullivan, was supposed to have caused a lot of fuss with the British around here," Tony said. "And the British General Burgoyne had Ethan Allen and his Green Mountain boys completely surrounded right at this spot. Allen was able to find his way through the woods while Burgoyne kept getting lost. The Americans slipped out of the trap, and a few months later teamed up with Benedict Arnold and Dan Morgan to defeat Burgoyne down at Saratoga." He puckered his forehead. "That was in 1777, just about the time Captain James Cook was making his discovery voyages along the Alaska coast." He looked sideways at

Rufe. "Guess I'm the only teacher who mixes up history dates—Revolutionary War and Alaska."

Even while he was slipping along forest trails that had bewildered and dismayed General Burgoyne, Tony's thoughts were turning to the Northland. He looked intently at the smooth green mounds of Elephant Mountain, wondering how it would compare with the terrors of the Chugach Mountains guarding the Copper River country in Alaska.

The sun beat down fiercely, burning the two explorers as they clambered over the deadfall of logs lining the shores of the lake. When they stopped for a noonday meal at Kitchel Bay, Rufe Snyder started to unlace his boots. "Bet there's one thing you won't be able to do in Alaska, Tony."

"What's that?"

"Go in swimming like I'm going to do right now."

They dove into the cold green waters, racing each other, staying underwater for a long time while they explored the murky bottom. Finally they floated quietly on their backs, looking up to the clear sky.

"Tony, why do you keep talking about Valdez and the Copper River country?"

Tony rolled about in the water before answering. "That's where all the excitement is, right now. It's become the outfitting point for all the Interior country. There are trails that go up right into the country where they had the last gold strikes—up around Fairbanks."

"Is that how Jack London went in?"

Tony shook his head. "He went in over the White Pass, before they finished the railroad four years ago. He went through Dead Horse Gulch and on over to

Lake Bennett in British Columbia. That's where the prospectors built boats and rafts and floated their gear down to Carcross and along the Yukon to Dawson. Jack London was pretty good in the water. He made more money piloting the Miles Canyon Rapids than he did prospecting."

Rufe rolled over and over in the water like a frisking seal. Then he stood almost upright, moving his hands and feet slowly. "Well, if they did it—why can't we?"

"Why can't we do what?"

"Make a raft and pretend we're floating down Lake Bennett and shooting the Miles Canyon Rapids?"

As soon as lunch was out of the way, they swung axes on the fallen spruce, pine and birch that lined the shore, and built a sturdy raft. Then, with their gear aboard, they pushed out on the still waters of Lake George.

For the next three days they drifted southward, pretending they were comrades of Jack London on his epic journey from the headwaters of the Yukon to the wide flat delta where it empties into the Bering Sea.

"I've never had so much fun in my life," Rufe said. "Someday, you're going to look up from your claim, and there I'll be—big as life." He looked again at Tony. "What's wrong? You've been quiet all day."

Tony didn't answer.

On the last night they camped on Little Island. Tony was quiet as he cleaned the fish they had caught. Rufe watched intently as his teacher rubbed the large chunks of fish in grated bread crumbs, and then fried them to a golden brown.

"Looks good," Rufe said. "I could eat a dozen."

Abruptly, Tony rose from the fire and walked down

to the lake. He listened to the small sounds of the water moving about his feet. Rufe followed. "What is it, Tony? What's wrong? Are you leaving soon, going to Alaska?"

Dimond shook his head. He struck one hand harshly into the other. "No. That's the trouble. Looks like I'm never going. It will take me another two years to save what I need."

"Why don't you go without the money? Just—well, just pack up and go?"

Tony shook his head. "The beaches at Nome and the wharf at Valdez are crowded with men who never even got started. If there's one thing I've learned from my reading, Rufe, it's this—a man who goes North without being prepared is a fool." He stood erect. "It's not going to happen to me."

"What will you do?"

"I don't know. Keep saving. Keep hoping that some-day I can really get north—and not just pretend."

All that night, while Rufe slept, Tony sat by the fire, watching the sparks leap into the air and disappear, watching the slow advance of ashes that dampened the glow of the embers. It was that way with his dream of Alaska. It was fast disappearing.

CHAPTER THREE

/\

Tony sat with his back against the smooth trunk of an old birch tree. Instinctively he faced to the north. As the fire dropped lower and lower, with only an occasional flash of yellow life, the stars overhead grew brighter. He followed the long sweeping handle of the Big Dipper. His eyes measured the ladle, then leaped across a million light years of space to focus on the pale unwinking beacon of the North Star. He wondered how many men had followed that guide to adventure; how many others, like himself, had to be content with dreaming.

The darkly outlined tree boughs, weaving back and forth across the sky as the night breeze pushed them, had a hypnotic effect. Even while his eyes were open, he could feel himself drifting off to sleep.

"Tony! Tony!" He heard the voice calling from far away. "Tony! Wake up!" Then, coupled with the words, he felt the rough shaking on his shoulder. He put his hands up to defend himself and tumbled off to one side.

"Tony!" Rufe said insistently. "Wake up! Look at these! All over my face and shoulders!"

Tony sat upright, grimacing with the sudden ache that stabbed at his backbone. "Must've slept on rocks," he said aloud, rubbing his side tenderly.

"Tony! Can't you hear me? Look!"

He looked closely at the young face. He opened his eyes wide in astonishment, then leaped to his feet, grinning. "Rufe! You've got chicken pox! Let's get you home!"

They ate their last meal by the lake, anchored the raft securely, then swung down the road heading for the train station. On the long ride home, while Rufe counted the red marks popping up like volcanoes, Tony gave way to discouragement. He was sure that his careful planning had all been wasted. He'd probably stay with schoolteaching for the rest of his life.

He turned Rufe over to his father. "Brought back a souvenir we weren't expecting, Mr. Snyder. Rufe has the fanciest case of chicken pox I've ever seen."

"Welcome home, Rufe," the older man said. "You've got lots of company. Between you and your sister you've got enough spots to stretch clear over to Albany."

Tony kept his word and finished out the school year. But a few days later he said good-by to his mother and father at the farm in Palatine Bridge. He walked out to the haymow where his younger brother Herbert was searching for a hen's nest.

"Good-by, Herbie."

"Good-by, Tony." There was a moment of uncomfortable silence, then Herbie asked, "After you see the Fair in Saint Louis, you going further West?"

"I think so. I'll write and tell you. Don't let Mom and Dad worry."

There was a brief handshake. Impulsively, Herbie kissed Tony on the cheek, then ran into the house to hide his tears.

Attending the Exposition at Saint Louis was the first of several moves Tony made in the next eight months, working and sight-seeing almost without purpose.

He went south to New Orleans, then, restless, turned north again to New York City. It was there he felt a first glimmering interest in the study of Law. He worked several months in a law office, literally gulping down the information hidden in the thick, musty books that littered the office. He had almost made up his mind to continue with his studies and prepare for the New York bar examination, when one of the many letters came from Joe Murray, his friend in Alaska. He left New York City, for the pull was westward, toward the Pacific Coast and the distant land of Alaska.

In the winter of 1904 he worked as a farmhand in Illinois. He loved the horses that were on Mr. Beyers' farm. Every evening he rode for miles looking west toward the setting sun. He was gentle, kind, generous, full of good humour, industrious and courteous. But he was stirred always with the restlessness of youth and the pull of Alaska. He spent his nights reading everything he could about the Territory.

When he stopped a team of runaway mules, pulling a mowing machine, by stunning one of them with a pitchfork blow, he was promoted to mule driver. He wrote home, telling his father of the farming methods used in the Middle West, telling of the mammoth hay rakes and the other pieces of farm equipment he had not known at home. "The man who works hard and tends to business every minute of his working day is a rarity and is treated accordingly." Then, at the end of his letter was a statement he repeated over and over again. "I still want to go to Alaska. Joe Murray writes and tells me what a wonderful country it is."

One cold night he boarded a train that was pointed toward the Pacific Ocean, more than half a continent away. After he had paid for his train tickets there were only thirty-five dollars left in his wallet.

At nine o'clock in the evening, when night was black over Chicago, the train eased from the station, moving north toward the line of barrier states separating the United States and Canada. The conductor leaned over as he picked up Tony's ticket and pointed outside to a thin white line of silver in the darkness. "Mississippi River," he said. "Out on the platform you can smell the dogwood."

But Tony fell asleep, stiff and rigid in the uncomfortable seat, one leg placed protectively over the traveling bag.

While he slept the train creaked and groaned through the night, climbing northward toward St. Paul. With the first light of dawn, Tony munched on a sandwich, staring at the unfolding countryside. When he saw the green farmlands and fat dairy cattle of Minnesota, he felt a momentary disappointment. "Looks like Amsterdam County in New York," he thought. "Where are the Indians?"

He confided his thoughts to the dark-skinned news

butcher who came through the car selling sandwiches and hot coffee.

"Take a good look, farmer boy. You're talking to one. I'm a full-blooded Sioux. Lot easier working this train than living on the reservation."

Tony sat back, abashed. For the rest of the long journey, more than twenty-two hundred miles, whenever Harry White Rivers came through the car he stopped and talked to Tony. He pointed to the grotesque buttes on both sides of the right-of-way. "Those are the Black Hills of North Dakota. My people used to hide in there before they gave up the fight and went on a reservation. I was born outside of Fort Abercrombie over there to the left." Later, for Tony's wide-eyed appreciation, he pointed to the horizon. "Sitting Bull is buried over there. Fort Yates. He died thirteen, fourteen years ago."

Tony looked at Harry White Rivers. "Was your Dad with Sitting Bull when Custer. . . ?"

"Uh-huh. He doesn't talk much about it now. He's an old man." He scuffed his foot on the worn carpeting of the train. "You people call it a massacre. We think it was a great victory."

When the train eased slowly into the station at Billings, Montana, Harry invited Tony to step off the train with him. "Calamity Jane Billings used to put on shows for the passengers coming through. Shoot pennies in the air. Things like that. Well," he said, looking about, "the town's not the same since she died last year."

It took the train nearly twenty hours to cross the eight-hundred-mile width of Montana, climbing from the flat plains of the eastern section over three mountain ranges of the Rockies into Idaho. The long, snaking train followed the Yellowstone River trail that Lewis and Clark had blazed almost a century before.

The train raced downhill into Spokane, then over the arid regions of western Washington to the lush Yakima Valley crammed with apple, peach, pear and cherry orchards. Then it cut a pathway through the Cascade Mountains, and tunneled under the rocks, holding as a guiding beacon the white peak of Mount Rainier, towering 14,508 feet into the air.

Tony's excitement increased as the train followed the course of the turbulent Green River through the dense forest of fir, cedar, spruce and hemlock so characteristic of the western part of the State of Washington. Finally the train stopped in the red-bricked splendor of King Street Station in Seattle.

Tony was desperately homesick. After attending Mass at the Cathedral, he walked to the massive building that housed the post office.

"Mail for Anthony Dimond, please," he asked at the general delivery window.

The clerk shuffled a handful of letters, then shook his head. "Sorry—wait a minute. Here's one. Couldn't hardly tell." He shoved a letter through the grill. On the envelope were a half dozen addresses scratched out. "This has been following you all over the country."

Tony wrinkled his forehead in puzzlement at the postmark, *Valdez, Alaska.*

With a sudden movement he ripped the letter open. In his haste, he tore the enclosed sheet in two pieces. Just then the big swinging doors of the post office opened, creating a draft, and one of the torn halves fluttered outside in the wind. Tony raced for it, fell down the stone steps, and skidded to the sidewalk. He reached, missed and fell flat, holding the runaway portion under his chest. Then, cautiously, he secured the paper and matched it to the other half clutched in his hand.

"Glory," he whispered when he read the message. "Glory!" Without another word, he leaped to his feet, raced inside the post office for his bag, and was off like the wind. He ran down the street, looking at the lettering on each window as he fled by.

He dashed breathlessly into the telegraph office. He spread the torn letter on the counter and read it once more:

Mr. Dimond:

Is this your traveling bag that's been in our storage room for the past eight months? We're charging you storage. What do you want done with the bag?

S. Kleve, Proprietor,
Phoenix Hotel, Valdez, Alaska

Tony wrote the reply on the telegraph blank:

HOLD BAG UNTIL MY ARRIVAL THANKS TONY DIMOND

He shoved the blank across the counter, "Please send this message," he said to the operator.

The telegraph operator adjusted his green eyeshade and nodded his head. "Two dollars and fifty cents."

Tony dipped his hand into his pocket. Suddenly his muscles tensed, and he started searching frantically through his pockets. Then, remembering, he quickly unlaced his right boot, kicked it off and dug deep inside.

He pulled out a crumpled bill, smoothed it, and placed it on the counter. "Five dollar bill," he said.

The operator picked up the bill gingerly and dropped it into the till. He pushed the change back to Tony. "I've seen money in funny places. . . ."

Tony grinned and stooped to lace his boot.

Then he went out and breathed deeply of the rain-washed air of Seattle.

There were still sixteen hundred miles of ocean barring him from Valdez. He sniffed appreciatively the clean smell of wide Puget Sound. Delivery vans, pulled by stocky horses, clattered over the street. There was a stiff breeze blowing from the Sound. Tony heard the whistle of steamships drifting from a distance. He turned to the left and looked down the steep hill that fell away sharply to the waterfront. There, alongside wooden piers, were a score of steamships and sailing vessels, all of them moving restlessly on the tide, straining at the hawsers that kept them tied to the land.

Far out in Elliott Bay a small ship moved cautiously toward the shore. Beyond, busy ferryboats etched snake paths across the water. Far away, on the opposite shore, a towering mountain lifted a snow cone high into the air.

All about, as Tony walked the streets, his bag banging against his knees, was an air of excitement. On the stores of First Avenue were glaring signs and banners.

ALASKA OUTFITTERS! BEST IN THE WEST!
GOLD PANS, SHOVELS, PICKS
TENTS, PARKAS, INDIAN-MADE SNOWSHOES
BLANKETS, DOG SLEDS, BOOTS
LAST CHANCE! LAST CHANCE!

"Golly," Tony thought to himself, "maybe I won't be able to buy any of my outfit in Valdez. There's nothing left. These fellows have everything."

He was so intent on looking at the outfits in the windows that he stumbled against a sidewalk sign placed before a livery stable: SLEEPING SPACE IN HAYLOFT, FIFTY CENTS. He peered into the large bay windows of a hotel and saw small iron cots jammed side by side in the lobby. Seattle was full to the bursting point.

Men, like himself, newly arrived in the bustling city, crowded the sidewalks. Some strode along quickly, purposefully. Others seemed in a daze, bewildered by shouting voices, the hooting trains, the clattering drays, and the low, reverberating cry of the steamship whistles.

Tony sat for a moment on the steps of the post office, and watched the endless parade. Then, remembering that he had not written to his parents, he scribbled a short note. "I'm on my way, Mother and Dad," he wrote. "This time I'm really going to Alaska. The mails are very irregular up there. Please don't worry if you don't hear from me for long periods at a time. I'll be thinking of all of you every minute while I'm gone—well, nearly!"

All of Seattle was in movement, heading down to noisy trestled Railroad Avenue. Ships were coming and going. Men were running forward and retreating. The motion was endless.

Tony sat on a high stool in a tiny café jammed between a ship chandler's and an Oriental silk importer's warehouse. The ponderous counterman pointed a stubby finger at him. "Breakfast is fifteen cents, and we're asking money before we serve. Been just too many bums come in here, eat us out of house and home, and slip on

board a ship to Alaska before we know what's what."
He leaned far over the counter and looked dubiously at
Tony's lone traveling bag. "Maybe you ain't. . . ."

"Yes, I am," Tony said hurriedly. "Here's the fifteen
cents. Can you tell me which of these ships is leaving
first for Alaska?"

"*Excelsior.* Pier Forty. Noon."

"Thanks!"

The counterman flicked a soiled towel at a big blue-
bottle fly that was hovering for a landing. "Didn't mean
to insult you—asking for payment in advance. Lunch is
twenty cents," he continued hopefully. "Dinner is
thirty."

"I'm going out on the *Excelsior.* I won't be back."

The counterman looked at him oddly. "Well, if you
change your mind. . . ."

Tony picked up his bag and walked through the narrow door. He picked his way cautiously through the
wagons and trains and people hurrying along under the
bows of sailing ships and steamers that hung directly
over the trestles.

He walked close to the thick bumper rail, immediately
above the oily waters. He kept looking at the big white
numerals painted on the cavernous pier sheds. He read
the names of the storm-beaten ships that were almost
within touching distance. The *Yukon,* the *Victoria,* the
Marriman, the *Islander,* the *Cape Spencer,* the *Excelsior.*
He stopped short.

Inside the tiny steamship office was the same air of
excitement and confusion that seemed an integral part of
Seattle from the moment he had stepped off the train.
Tony's ears rang with the babble of voices. He edged

closer and closer to the counter. Finally he looked through the grilled window to the harried clerk.

"I'd like to book passage to Valdez on the *Excelsior*," Tony said, holding his wallet firmly in his right hand.

"Forty dollars, first class. Twenty-three dollars, steerage."

"Steerage," Tony answered, counting the bills carefully. "When do you want to sail?"

"Today," Tony replied, breathing a deep sigh of relief as he spread the money on the counter. "I'm hoping to be in Valdez in. . . ."

The clerk looked at him sharply. "You ain't got a reservation?"

"Reservation?"

"Sure. You don't think you're just going to walk aboard that ship like it was a grocery store, do you? You got to put in a reservation. Ain't an empty berth northbound to Alaska, not for love'r money."

"I've got to go out—today!"

The clerk shoved Tony's money gently back through the grill. "The *Excelsior's* booked solid through June."

"That's three months from now!"

"And you're lucky I can find you space on that sailing. Most of these ships are booked solid through the summer. Sorry, young fellow." He looked over Tony's shoulder. "Next, please!"

CHAPTER FOUR

Tony walked uncertainly out of the door. Almost in a daze, he threaded through the traffic. Vans and horses and puffing trains rolled down Railroad Avenue like logs in a mountain stream. Alaska was disappearing again. He didn't have enough money to wait in Seattle until he could sail north.

"Get out of the way, you farmer!"

With a wild clattering of hoofs and the screeching of thick brake shoes on iron-shod wheels, a big dray thundered along the planks, the driver yelling angrily. Tony leaped to one side. He could see the trunks piled high on the rear of the dray, fat rolls of blankets and bulging barrels. On most of them were glaring red shipping labels with the words, *S. S. Excelsior, Pier 40*. Almost without thinking, Tony flipped his bag over the tailgate and pulled himself aboard. He slipped down out of sight between the trunks and barrels.

He could hear the driver shouting as the big wagon wove its way through the traffic. Then there was the hollow thumping of the horses' hooves on wood, and a

sudden rush of silence. The light faded, and the noise
of the dray was swallowed inside the pier shed. He
waited until the wagon slowed and the horses started to
back up, prodded by shouts and commands from the
driver. Then he slipped from the wagon and looked
about.

Stacked in rows on either side of the pier were huge
piles of boxes and trunks. Above each towering pile was
a wooden sign identifying a seaport destination in
Alaska. Ketchikan, Juneau, Cordova, Valdez, Nome.
Stevedores were moving in and out of the open doors
that led to the high sides of the wooden *Excelsior*. Barrels and boxes were slung over their shoulders. Trying
desperately to remain unnoticed, Tony slipped over to
the door, tossed his bag into a half-empty barrel, and
hoisted it on his shoulder. Then, his heart pounding, he
edged into the line of stevedores, walking unsteadily out
into the sunlight.

"Watch your footing, there, fellow!" the stevedore boss
bellowed. "You'll have that barrel in the drink!"

Tony placed one foot on the slanting gangplank,
hitched the barrel more securely on his shoulders, and
started upward. He followed the man before him, bending and winding about the hatches and winches, the
piles of goods, the lumber, the stacked telegraph poles.
Out of the corner of his eye, he saw the stevedore in the
lead give a heave and drop his box to the deck. Tony
followed his example, working and shoving at the barrel
until it lined up neatly with the others on the deck.
Then, reaching in, he quietly pulled out his traveling
bag, lifted it to his shoulder, and walked determinedly
forward.

He expected any moment to hear a voice call to him, to have a hand reach forward to stop him. He climbed a ladder of iron steps, set his bag down, and mingled with the crowd that thronged the rail of the ship. To all outward appearances, he was one of the passengers jammed into the two-hundred foot length of the *Excelsior*.

For another hour Tony waited by the rail, hardly daring to move. He watched the endless stream of excited passengers edging up the gangplank. The busy stewards ran back and forth on last-minute errands. The steamship officials, long white sheets of paper fluttering in their hands, raced back and forth, calling aloft to the stern-faced captain high above on the bridge.

A dozen fat cows were driven through the open door of the pier shed. They were shoved, bawling and kicking, along a lower gangplank and herded to pens below deck. In rapid succession, several dozen pigs, a like number of sheep, and endless crates of chickens came aboard. On a barge fifty yards away from the *Excelsior* scores of horses were being loaded, their high-pitched neighs of alarm adding to the general excitement.

Vast quantities of hay were hoisted aboard, cabbages and crates of fruit, ice and whole carcasses of beef. The stream of passengers dwindled. A few excited individuals still scurried about. A last reluctant steer was forced along the gangplank by a twist of its tail.

There was a sibilant hissing of steam.

"WHO-OOOOO-OOOO!"

A little man standing beside Tony clapped his hands to his ears and staggered backward. All the men, and the few women, crowded aboard the *Excelsior* threw back their heads. Their eyes were on the long, flaring plume of steam that gushed from the whistle on the smoke-stack. An electric feeling of excitement ran through the crowd.

Tony slipped close to the rail, hanging far over.

Longshoremen ran to the thick hawsers fore and aft. They lifted them from the stubby bits on the pier, letting them drop with a dull, wet thud into the Sound. Steam winches sputtered, and the dripping hawsers clattered through the pipes and on deck where seamen coiled them in neat piles.

"What's that?" the little man demanded apprehensively of Tony. Far beneath them there was a shuddering rumble, a faint quivering that took hold of the entire ship and shook it with a forceful motion.

"Engines," Tony explained. In the ignorance of the little man he felt a glow of wide knowledge. "They're starting the engines down in the engine room. Look astern; you can see the water churning from the propellors."

An officer of the *Excelsior*, gold-braided cap perched jauntily on the side of his head, brushed past, looking oddly at Tony. At that moment, someone at the rail yelled, "We're moving!" The officer hurried away.

Water boiled at the stern. The little ship backed away in a tight circle, moved ahead, and edged into Elliott Bay. The crowds at the rail were silent, looking at the dwindling figures standing on the pier. A few hands lifted and waved in farewell. The white faces of those left behind gradually blurred and faded indistinctly into the red paint of the pier.

The cowboys, painters, cooks, clerks, ranchers, miners, actors, doctors, gamblers, schoolteachers, reporters, dance hall girls, housewives, railroad men, merchants and sailors were jammed in the small ship. They looked out at the water widening between them and the mainland. The business buildings and the homes crowding on the seven hills of Seattle began to fade back into the green mask of the trees that crowded the city. For a moment Tony didn't want to speak. He didn't want anyone to talk. He kept looking at the mainland fading away, and his thoughts were leaping the width of the continent to New York State, to his family, and to Rufe Snyder.

"Get 'em out of there! Drag 'em up! Hurry!"

There was a commotion on the forward deck, and the crowd, Tony among them, surged forward. Up from the hold came a sorry procession of figures, young men and old, looking about, blinking in the sunlight. A few of them clutched packages or bags in their hands. The officer with the gold braid on his cap herded them into a corner. "You danged stowaways," he bellowed, "give us more trouble than a shipload of monkeys! Anybody can't swim? Then over the side all of you! Up you go, now—no stopping!"

A few voices lifted in protest, but the stowaways, some of them as though practised in the art, clambered up to the low rail, leaped outward and plumped into the cold waters.

"They'll drown!" Tony called, horrified.

"You worried, buddy?" The ship's officer snapped the question at Tony, looking at him quizzically. "We take care of 'em."

Around the bow of the ship, which was just getting

underway, a small dory appeared, shepherding the swimmers to shore like so many stray cattle.

Out in the stream the *Excelsior* swung about slowly while the compass was checked. Then, with a final blare of the whistle, the engines commenced an authoritative throb, and the journey to Alaska started.

His bag still banging against his knees, Tony picked his way through the incredible junk piled on the decks. Behind him followed the little man, a paper bag clutched defensively in his hand.

Standing in the bow Tony watched the green face of Magnolia Bluff drop to the stern. He looked always to the north, to the islands that blocked Puget Sound from the Pacific Ocean and Alaska.

"Valdez," the little man said.

"Pardon me?"

"I'm going to Valdez," the little man said belligerently. "I'm opening a dress shop. For ladies."

"That's nice." Tony wished he would go away.

The white chain of the Cascades filled the eastern horizon.

"It's not nice. My partner couldn't come. I got his ticket." He waved the green ticket in Tony's face. "I'm going to lose money before I start."

Tony reached out and took the fluttering paper. "You won't lose money. I'll buy it." He thrust the money into the little man's hand. Then he turned away, listening intently to the throbbing of the propellor. Every cut of the blade into the water brought him closer to Alaska.

That night he stretched, sleepless, in a narrow bunk. His new acquaintance tossed and turned in the bunk below him.

With the approach of dawn on the ninth day out of Seattle, groups of passengers huddled on the decks, their backs turned to the chill winds while they discussed their plans for the coming assault on Alaska.

"Give me two years," one loud-mouthed passenger said. "That's all I need. I'll rip what I can from the country, and get out so fast you won't be able to see me for smoke."

"Six months is all I ask," another volunteered. "Dig it deep, and dig it fast. That's my motto. Why," the man exclaimed from the depths of his fur collar, "I've heard tell of gold strikes up in the Interior and over in Canadian territory where they got one hundred dollars worth of dust from a single pan of gravel! Imagine that!"

"How about these lucky fellows that found as much as ten thousand dollars worth of nuggets in one little pocket? That's what I'm after!"

"You fellows are greedy," another voice chimed in. "Most pans only average five, six dollars—that's enough for me. Slow, steady way to get rich—maybe four, five months."

"Listen, fellow," a deep voice boomed, "I didn't come up to this forsaken country for a five-dollar pitch. Million dollars in one year—that's what I'm after. And it's been done, too," the voice added belligerently.

"One hundred million dollars been pulled out of the Klondike just in the past seven years," an awed voice broke in. "Why, they shipped that gold out in gallon oilcans! And it belonged to ordinary fellows, men just like me'n you, 'n all the others."

Tony listened, his head swimming. "How do you stake a claim?" he asked.

"Nothing to it," a burly fellow answered. "Neighbor of mine, he just got back from the Klondike, told me all about it." The big man held out his clenched fists descriptively, "You drive in these four-foot stakes, two hundred fifty feet apart, on the creek you're going to work, and you go back five hundred feet from the water, and drive two others. Get your name on the stakes, and hurry up and register with the Commissioner. That's all there is to it," he finished. He grinned and made digging motions with his big hands. "Then you start digging." He winked at Tony. "What's your plans, son?"

"I don't know," Tony answered. "I just don't know. Guess when I get my bag and money from the Phoenix Hotel I'll be able to think better."

The little man who shared the cabin with Tony looked at him craftily. "Sell things to these miners—that's how to get rich fast. That's what I'm going to do. You can go dig the gold," he said, "I got honest, legitimate ways of getting the gold after you dig it."

Tony shook his head. "I don't want to do that." He grinned sheepishly. "I guess all I want is adventure."

"Humph!"

Suddenly the seas calmed, and the little ship followed an unseen path into Prince William Sound. Tony was on deck, looking to the high wall of the Chugach Mountains with their dozens of glaciers creeping down to the sea. The ship crept into the landlocked harbor, pushed close to a wall of mountains, and inched toward the newly built wooden pier thrust far out from the gravel flats immediately surrounding the Bay. Groups of townsfolk moved down from the town. Hawsers swung out. The *Excelsior* was tied securely.

Tony was one of the first off the ship. He paused only long enough to whisper a prayer of gratitude for his arrival in Alaska. Then he almost ran up to the town.

He bumped into a stocky figure leaning against the wall of a wooden building.

"I'm sorry," Tony said. "I'm looking for the Phoenix Hotel. Can you tell me where. . . ."

"Sure thing, son. I'll tell you." The miner pointed with his stubby fingers to a charred heap of embers. "There she is. Burned to the ground just three days ago."

CHAPTER FIVE

Tony stood before the charred, soggy remains of the Phoenix Hotel. He was speechless. He could think only that he was sixteen hundred miles from Seattle, forty-six hundred miles from home, and all he had left was one dollar and thirty-five cents.

The miner who had pointed out the remnants of the hotel ambled across the muddy street. "She was a duzzy," he said in admiration. "Burned for three hours." He patted a bedraggled sofa sitting in the snow. "I saved this all by myself. Everything else burned."

Tony thanked him and walked away. He was hungry—so hungry that he was able to forget the terrible disappointment he had just experienced. His boots slipped on the snow-covered wooden sidewalks. He read aloud the names of the saloons and gambling halls jammed along McKinley Street: Montana, Horseshoe, Keystone, and the Bohemian.

His friend, Joe Murray, had been here in Valdez—but that was almost a year before. He kept looking about, hoping he might run into him. Gamblers and ruffians crowded the sidewalk, the tents, hotels and crude wooden buildings hastily built to take care of the hundreds who were pouring into the small town. He saw a young girl standing in the doorway of MILLER's GROCERY. Her arms were crowded with packages, and she was looking doubtfully at the horses and sleighs jamming the snow-packed street.

"Can I help you, ma'am?" Tony asked.

She nodded and he took the packages and led the way through the deep drifts. There were freshly baked rolls in one of the open packages and Tony eyed them wistfully as he handed the packages back to the girl. Quickly she offered him one, and quickly he accepted.

"I don't think we'll miss one roll," she said. She nodded to the store across the narrow street. "That's my father's grocery. I'm Dorothea Miller. Maybe, if you need work—" She stopped speaking suddenly, turned and hurried away.

Tony finished the roll, lifting his eyes to the ring of white-shrouded mountains, the saw-toothed Chugach Range that completely dominated Valdez. Low under the snow clouds were vast fields of gray glaciers, melting and sending a vast quantity of water into Valdez Bay.

On the far side of the vicious peaks was the legendary Copper River, the swift, muddy stream that flowed through narrow canyons, past great cliffs of glacial ice and through a myriad of treacherous and shifting channels. The Copper River was the route to the Interior. Northward from its unexplored headwaters was a pass over the Alaska Range, opening to the winding Tanana River that led directly to the new gold strikes.

And no longer was gold alone the lure. Rumors of

tremendous copper finds, mountains of green ore worth
a fortune that waited only the coming of a railroad to
bring the treasures down to the sea, were causing a new
surge of excitement in Valdez.

"You, boy, you." The little man with the dress goods
collection blocked Tony's path. "You want a job, boy?
Or are you running off like all those crazy ones, climbing
over the mountain?"

Tony felt the change purse in his pocket. He was still
hungry. His money might buy one meal, perhaps two if
he were careful. He looked at the bolts of gingham trail-
ing in the snow. He shook his head regretfully. "Guess
I'm going to run off, just like the rest. Sorry."

A score of horses were being driven down the street
and herded into a makeshift corral. Alongside the activity, dripping with icicles, was the sign:

PACKERS WANTED
HIGH WAGES
COPPER RIVER DRAYING COMPANY
GOOD FOOD

Two hours later Tony, his stomach pleasantly full, was
trudging alongside a column of heavily burdened horses
that trod the wagon trail from Valdez. Some of the
animals had just arrived on the barge floating in Valdez
Bay. Others were gaunt veterans of the glacial trail.
Knobby bones showed through the lashings that held
the boxes and bundles precariously on the backs of the
sixteen horses. Three other hostlers besides Tony urged
the line forward.

With only a gentle prodding, the animals plodded

along methodically, aiming for the wall of mountains. Tony was soon soaked to the knees when the pack train forded the nameless streams spurting down from Valdez Glacier.

Up ahead, the boss packer led the way along the Robe River, then followed the flood plain of the Lowe River Valley into the rock walls of Keystone Canyon, thirteen miles beyond Valdez. At times the horses hesitated in the heavy growth of spruce and underbrush barring the way. Tony leaned against the flank of a tired horse and shoved. "Come along, fellow," he grunted. "I'm just as tired as you are."

The pack train climbed past the wide-spreading Horseshoe Falls. The nervous horses trod cautiously over the frail bridge that spanned Snowslide Gulch. Tony was breathing hard. It was a slow, steady upward climb past sheer rock walls towering a thousand feet above them. He kept looking about, wary of unexpected washouts and slides.

The pack train stopped for the night at Wortman's, nineteen miles from Valdez. Tony wolfed down the slabs of salmon that were served. With the other hostlers snoring about him, he stretched in a rude bunk, and started to think back over his first day in Alaska. But before he had the first picture formed, he was asleep.

Next morning, stiff and sore, he stood in the chill wind, helping load the horses that shuffled from the long cavern of stables. Then, following the lead of Tex, the boss packer, he walked stiff-legged out on the trail. He tried to shout gaily to the horses, but the wind and sleet struck deep into his marrow, and his tongue clove to the roof of his mouth. "Let's move faster," he muttered to the horse he was following closely, "We'll freeze to death in this country if we stop to think!"

For the first part of the journey, in the cold, snow-bowed caverns of the spruce forests, the horses were patient, plodding forward with little urging in a long line that snaked higher and higher on the mountain. When the footing became treacherous and slippery, and the noise of spring-touched waterfalls pounded down on them, some of the horses became nervous. These were the ones only a few weeks away from placid living on Washington and Oregon farms. They started neighing in fright, shying and rearing.

"Whoa, boy!" Tony called, hanging to the halter of a rearing bay. "Easy, fellow. I'm just as scared as you are."

One of the lean and gaunt horses near the head of the line stopped abruptly in its tracks, in the very center of Sheep Creek Suspension Bridge. "Get along, boy," Tony kept urging. "Get moving! You're holding up the parade."

The head packer, a tall Texan with skin the texture of worn saddle leather, watched Tony's efforts. "Don't bother no more, fellow," he said. "Just unload the horse."

Tony stripped the animal and prepared to lead him across the bridge. But he still refused to budge.

"Step back, fellow."

The Texan lifted his revolver and shot the horse through the head. "Help me push this critter off the bridge," he said.

They shoved, and the carcass fell in a wide, looping curve into the snow-covered gulch far below. Tony could see the bones of other pack horses thrust upward through the snow.

"This country," Tex said, "is sure rough on horses."

"Why did you do it?" Tony demanded.

Tex sighted down the barrel of his gun. "Don't get upset, son. These animals go crazy after a couple months on the trail. There ain't no power on earth going to get them moving once they make their minds up they ain't. So, you shoot 'em—and we get hostlers like you to pick up their load." He motioned to the gear that had been unloaded from the dead horse. "Get busy. We expect every man to pack a hundred and fifty pounds over the trail."

Tony shouldered the pack the Texan helped him to fashion. The straps dug into his shoulders. The head-band felt as though it were creasing a hollow in his forehead. He made every forward step with difficulty. The smooth, round rocks, made slick by the movement of glaciers ages before, were traps waiting to send him tumbling to the ground. Higher and higher they wound into the mountain barrier, inching forward to Thompson Pass, twenty-seven hundred feet in a nest of glacial ice. Tex came alongside Tony and with rough kindness helped adjust the straps of his pack. He pointed to the heap of dull-red rusting machinery barely visible above the wind-blown snow. "We're being paid two thousand dollars a ton to haul machinery into Fairbanks—and we still got to throw it away. Just humanly impossible to haul it over this mountain."

Struggling forward under the unaccustomed weight, Tony lost track of time. He was conscious only of the cruel wind that blew with a hurricane force, cutting his cheeks, nipping at his ears, slipping ice fingers inside his jacket. As they approached the elusive Thompson Pass, the wind roared with the fury of an icy hurricane, gathering speed as it rushed by the funnel of rocks that formed the Pass. At times the horses refused to move, standing with their heads turned to one side avoiding the wind. Grimly resolved not to give in, Tony huddled in the shelter of the big bay horse, hanging to the long, windblown tail as the gale shrieked down upon them. He pressed his face close to the horse's flank, grateful for the slight warmth.

"Horse," he said between chattering teeth, "if we don't start moving soon, they'll be naming the mountain after us—Dead Man's Peak."

With constant urging, the pack train finally topped the Pass. Tex brushed at the icicles that had formed in his eyebrows. "Little stone hut just ahead," he announced. "We'll stop there to eat and feed the horses. Then we gotta get going downhill. This wind'll kill you if you stay up here long enough."

The straps on the pack dug raw channels into Tony's shoulders. But, on the downgrade, he could almost forget the discomfort. Once the Pass was behind them, the wind settled. The pack train followed the tumbling Ptarmigan Creek past squat Worthington Glacier. At Ptarmigan Drop, Tony slipped from the pack and tumbled to the ground. He remembered dimly the Texan tossing a fur robe over him. Then he fell into an exhausted sleep.

The next day, fighting through softly falling snow, they used the Tsina River for a guide down to the twelve-hundred-foot altitude. It was a zigzag course, doubling back and forth to avoid the scores of hanging glaciers that formed an almost perfect circle around Valdez.

"Watch your footing, boy," the Texan called to Tony who was fording a rushing mountain stream. "You won't be the first man to drown in this creek if you go under. Careful."

Because the government wagon trail to Copper Center was blocked by slides, the pack train turned left at Stewart Creek. Far ahead, they saw the dirty gray of the tents of Klutina City dimly outlined against the pure white of the snow on the surrounding mountains. The horses picked up speed, winding in single file between the crowding tents. The hostlers unloaded the heavy freight, and prepared immediately for the return to Valdez. From this point forward, after the spring break-up, the Klutina, leading to the Copper River, would afford easy water transportation for the assault on the two mountain ranges barring the way to the gold fields of the Interior.

When Tony pocketed the wages handed him by the Texan, he rubbed his shoulders tenderly and said, "I'm not going back. Another trip like that and you'd be pushing me off Sheep Creek Bridge."

The Texan tried to hide his disappointment. "Suit yourself, Dimond. We get thirty cents a pound packing in from Valdez. We feed regular—horses and men. You won't find that true in this madhouse." He gestured contemptuously toward the snow-bowed tents of Klutina City. He turned abruptly and left.

It was close to darkness, and the endless snow clouds were dropping lower, hiding the peaks of the mountains. Tony dug a sandwich from his pocket and chewed on it thoughtfully. "I've lived on sandwiches clear from New

York State," he thought, grinning to himself. Yellow lanterns gleamed dimly through the soiled canvas of the tents. Farther away the sound of loud voices and clanking music filled the air.

The loud, smacking report of a rifle snapped in the air. There was a sudden silence along the irregular row of tents, then the chorus of noises thickened and deepened. Tony walked down the rutted space between the tents, lonely and dispirited. In all of Alaska there was not one person to give him greeting. He stumbled over hummocks of ice and freshly cut tree stumps, moving down to the shore of the frozen lake.

Lake Klutina was a wide space in the Klutina River. Ten miles from the tent city it narrowed abruptly, plunged through a steep gorge, and raced headlong to a meeting with the Copper River.

A fierce wind, born high on the slopes of Tazlina Glacier, raced across the flat ice of the lake. Tony crawled under an overturned skiff on the bank and burrowed under a heap of burlap bags. On the trail in from Valdez they had passed disheartened gold seekers heading back to the seacoast. He wondered uneasily if he would be one of the many men defeated by the towering mountains and the endless glaciers. "I won't give in," he said. He listened to the angry growlings of his empty stomach, then fell into a shivering sleep.

The frantic screams of quarreling blue jays ripped Tony from sleep. He crawled from the skiff and shivered. He stood uncertainly in the half-light of the new day, looking first toward the tent city, then far over the smooth ice of the lake. In the middle of the ice, he saw gray, sullen waters, a log floating, then a white object drifting. Tony's heart beat wildly.

"It's a man! Someone's fallen through!"

He ran out on the ice toward the center of the lake.

When Tony came closer, he slid forward on his stomach. He leaned over, grasped the white object, and lifted. The ice creaked dangerously. Tony heaved again and a waterlogged sack of flour came out.

Back on shore a man, dripping wet, waited his return.

"You all right?" Tony asked, leaping forward.

The dripping man nodded. "Lost my gear, everything I own."

Suddenly he blinked. "Managed to get ashore." He grinned weakly. "Guess that's the important thing." Then he shook himself like a bedraggled dog. He offered his hand dazedly to Tony. "My name's Johnson, Bill Johnson. Doesn't matter." He looked up at the mountains, his eyes blinking rapidly as though he were fighting back the tears. "This country's beat me once too often. I'm getting out."

He turned and almost ran away.

He was no sooner out of sight than Tony spied another fifteen-pound bag of flour floating in the water. He went out and rescued the bag. He knew the outer shell would have caked hard, protecting the inner contents. Beyond was another sack; then a small keg of molasses. One after the other Tony pulled them on the ice. He looked around eagerly for any other objects that might be floating in the water.

Back on shore he spread his salvaged goods to dry. He looked about for the owner of the skiff, but Klutina

City was still wrapped in sleep under the shelter of its dingy white tents.

Tony made a pack of his water-soaked cargo, and started to walk unsteadily along Mosquito Street, the main avenue in the temporary city. On a large tent with wooden sides was hung a sign: "Supplies." A stove pipe thrust through the canvas was smoking vigorously. A bald-headed man was kneeling in the street, vigorously polishing a saucepan. Tony dumped the watery sacks in front of him. "How much will you pay me for this stuff?" he asked.

The pan polisher looked sharply at Tony, then poked a suspicious finger into the sacks. "Ruined," he said.

"They're not. They're dry inside."

The finger poked again. "Twenty dollars."

"And all the breakfast I can eat?"

"And all the breakfast you can eat—but only two eggs, mind you."

"It's a deal. Where do I sit?"

While Tony munched contentedly on his breakfast, he looked in astonishment at the price list:

FLOUR	$12.50 a sack
SUGAR	.40 a pound
MILK	.50 a can
HAM AND BACON	.40 a pound

"Better get a job fast," he said to himself.

The owner loomed over him. "If you don't mind risking your neck out on the lake, I'll buy everything you bring in."

Tony shook his head. "No, thanks. There must be a better way to make a living in this camp."

He walked down the street, whistling. A little dog came running from one of the tents, barking fiercely as he made for Tony's boot. Suddenly he stopped and wagged his tail. Tony leaned down and patted him gratefully. "Thanks, fellow."

CHAPTER SIX

Tony heard an excited yipping and saw a row of wet noses thrust through the openings in a strong wooden pen. Above was lettered in crude fashion:

GOOD DOGS FOR SALE
SEE ME
IF YOU WANT TO GET
TO THE TANANA FIRST

There were loud voices raised in argument. Tony walked toward a tight group of men clustered before the tent restaurant.

"Don't see we ever have to use the river at all, not at all," a prospector with a voice and manner as thin as a reed exclaimed. He thumped himself on his hollow chest. "Why, man as strong as me could take off and walk in a straight line right over them mountains and glaciers."

"That's right, Sam. Just too much time wasted hanging around these rivers. They tell me the land across the mountains is as flat as a pancake. Anybody with half a mind could hike across the tundra and be in the Tanana Valley before he even got his wind up."

Tony listened in astonishment. So well had he prepared for this journey north that he had taken it for granted everyone knew the dangers awaiting beyond the mountains. He looked to a weather-beaten miner who sucked on a straw, smiling at the tirade of the newcomers.

"You boys talk big, but this here country is bigger. Nobody wants to get up to the Tanana Valley faster'n me, and I ain't aiming to waste no time, either."

"Then whyn't you show us the way north?" the thin man demanded. "Whyn't we just start hiking?"

The miner pulled his straw from his mouth and pointed it in the general direction of the mountains. "I climbed those mountains between here and Valdez with Captain Abercrombie seven years ago. Only an act of God we weren't all lost—first Americans to get across. Lot of people who tried to come over those glaciers after us just died—froze, fell down cliffs, and got buried under avalanches. They slipped into crevasses in the glaciers and weren't ever seen again. Why do you think we abandoned that trail and started slipping down creeks and rivers, circling nearly all around just to get to Copper Center?"

"Well," the thin man answered, hesitating, "maybe it ain't so easy to hike over mountains and glaciers, but what about the tundra?" he demanded triumphantly. "You can't tell me about that country killing people. Anybody knows it's as flat as the palm of my hand."

The straw chewer snorted. "Flat! Maybe if you had wings like a bird and flew over it—but just you try walking! There's hummocks high as your knee every foot of the way. You'll fall and twist your leg, and be danged lucky you don't break it the third step. Where there's no hummock you got jack pine so dang thick you can't pitch a pot of beans three feet let alone try to get through. So many rivers they ain't got names for them yet. And mosquitoes!" His eyes bulged in horror just at the thought. "Mosquitoes so thick you can swirl a knife through the air and draw blood. They start biting—man, how they bite, even your eyeballs. They'll kill you, that's what they'll do. They'll just plain and simple kill you, them mosquitoes."

"No mosquitoes now," the little man said defensively.

"Didn't say they was. Summertime. But even now, no dog teams can get across what you call flat country. When we get started inland, you want to stay alive, follow the rivers."

Tony had heard enough and he went off to find a place to live. Three other gold-seekers invited him to share their shack. At midnight they were all still hammering and sawing, shoving temporary bunks into every corner of the small wooden building. "Keep that fire nice and low," one of them grumbled. "Don't want to be fried before I even get to the Interior."

Another sat by a candle squinting at a frayed newspaper. "It's the little print that gets me," he muttered. "Them big letters I can spell out easy."

Tony rose from his bunk. "Let me try."

"This afternoon," he read aloud, "Congress authorized the first funds for new wagon roads in Alaska. First work will be done on the trail from Valdez to the gold fields of the Tanana Valley."

"What's funds mean?" one of the men demanded.

"Money," Tony explained.

"Then whyn't they say so?"

"How come if they got a new wagon road we're stuck in here in the mountains trying to crawl through like a bunch of billy goats?"

Tony looked at the date on the paper. "This was written one month ago. It takes time to get equipment up from the States. Might be another year. . . ."

"Humph! By that time I'll be back in Wisconsin loaded with enough gold to buy me a dairy farm spot cash."

Tony looked at the man. It was a sentiment he had heard expressed a hundred times since landing in Valdez. Get the gold, get out, get home. He tried to think of words in protest, but one of the men nudged him gently on the shoulder. "Get along with the reading, son."

"Two more ships have been sunk in the passage between Puget Sound and Alaska. The demand for lighthouses. . . ."

There was a hush in the tiny shack. Hammers were dropped; saws were put aside. One miner gently knocked the ashes from his pipe into the palm of his hand and squeezed into the group around the candlelight. Tony looked up in surprise. "Go on, son," the miner said. "Keep reading. Ain't heard no news from the States for eight weeks."

The next morning when Tony stepped outside the door of the shack, skim ice had formed on the pools about the doorway. The snow crown on the crowding mountains had crept lower. There was a stillness in the air that he had never noticed before. He shivered and walked down Mosquito Avenue. When he thrust his head through the flap of Jess Morton's tent restaurant, the owner was staring morosely at a splintered heap of china dishes scattered about the wooden floor.

"That dang dog," he said. "I caught him up on the table. I give him a wallop, and he sailed right into the dishes. Now just where'm I going to find more dishes? It'll put me out of business, that's what it'll do."

"Make the customers supply their own. Isn't a man in camp doesn't have some cooking gear. That'll give you time to send back to Valdez for replacements. . . ."

Jess Morton's face brightened. "By golly, you got something, boy. I'll paint me a sign right away. Pull up and have breakfast on me."

He went down the rows of tables, shaking vigorously at the blanketed forms stretched out on the hard surface. "Wake up, wake up! Come on, up you come!"

One after the other the figures stirred. Men sat upright on the tables, rubbing their eyes, gaping about.

"Can't let these men sleep outside in the cold," Jess explained to Tony defensively. "And at fifty cents a night —these tables'll soon pay for themselves using them as beds." He brushed virtuously at the table just vacated by a sleeper. "And you mind how we keep them sure sharp clean, too. Sanitary, that's what this place is. Sit down. Make yourself comfortable."

When Tony had finished his breakfast, he carried the lone dish back and cleaned it. "You've got a skiff down by the saw mill," he said. "I'd like to buy it."

"Ain't for sale."

"Why? You're in business. You won't be moving."

"That's what you say. I was in business in Dawson and Fort Yukon, up in Nome and down in Valdez. I'm hang-

ing my pots and pans wherever there's a bunch of fools
willing to pay outlandish prices for a hot meal. I'm here
today and gone tomorrow, and when I get what I'm aiming for, I'm leaving this country forever."

"But why? Why not stay in business?"

Jess Morton looked at Tony, shaking his head. "Don't
be foolish, boy. People come to Alaska. Don't nobody
stay here."

"That's wrong."

"Maybe—but I ain't the one to philosophize about it.
Tell you what," he said reflectively, scratching his chin,
"you want that skiff real bad, I won't swap it for money.
Got lots of that. Can you shoot?"

"Some."

Jess reached behind the wooden door for a rifle. "Get
out in the hills and see what you can knock down with
this. When you drag it back, we'll talk about the skiff."

He pulled open the door, looked out, and started in
fright. Then he leaped back inside, slammed shut the
door, and started to ram shells into the rifle.

"What's wrong?" Tony demanded.

"Injuns! By gum, Injuns! Hundreds of them! We're
being invaded!"

Tony brushed by the quivering man. He stood out in
the hard snow of the street that was gradually thawing
under the new sun. Strung out in single file, stretching
as far as he could see, was a line of Indians, blankets
slung over their shoulders, utensils clattering at their
waists. Braided hair dropped from the felt hats perched
on their heads. There was a score of solemn-faced children in the line, bright eyes darting from right to left
as they passed through the tent city.

"Copper River Indians," Tony said quietly over his shoulder. "Tex told me about them."

Cowards, Tex had said of the three hundred survivors of the Chitina tribe. Yet, pressed for an explanation, he had been vague as to the reason why this handful of once-brave men had been so quiet and distrustful, not only of the few white men with whom they came in contact, but even with the Coast Indians. Not until later did Tony discover the terrible wrongs suffered by these people at the hands of the Russian conquerors of Alaska. When Chitinas had been weakened by the Russians, the Coast Indians had swarmed over the mountains on raids, taking them as slaves. They stole the copper utensils and arms that were the treasures of the Chitinas, torturing them in a vain effort to learn the source of the copper.

Suddenly the long line stopped. The Indians gathered in tight groups, and sat upon the snow. The leader, a tall dark-skinned man about thirty-five years old, walked over. He looked past Tony's shoulder. "Coffee," he said.

"Sure." Tony stood by and let the Indian pass.

"Back up, you! Back up! Ain't no Indians coming in here to rob and steal me blind. Back up, you, and git!"

Tony reached out and quietly took the rifle from Morton. "Forget it, Jess. Bring the coffee." He turned to the Indian and thrust out his hand. "My name's Tony Dimond."

The Indian shook hands solemnly. "I am Goodlata. These are my people. We go to Valdez for supplies."

Jess placed a steaming cup of coffee before the tall Indian. "I'm watching," he muttered.

Goodlata glanced sideways at the rifle Tony held.

"I was going hunting," Tony said.

"Across the lake you will find bear. Skinny. Hungry."
Goodlata cradled the hot cup in his hand, stared intently
at the black liquid, and suddenly downed the entire cup
in one long gulp. He choked, stared at Tony, then walked
to the door. The tight circle of Indians unwound, formed
a line and trudged after their towering leader.

Jess Morton stood on his tiptoes, trying to peer over
Tony's shoulder. "Wasn't twenty years ago them people
massacred every white man they could lay their hands
on. Country won't be safe until we get rid of 'em."

"It's their country," Tony answered. "I'm leaving. I'll
take the skiff and hunt across the lake as Goodlata said."

Jess Morton shook his head. "You ain't going no place
with my rifle. With them Indians around I'm keeping
this real close. Ain't nobody going to slip in and murder
me, they ain't."

Tony started to protest. "That's ridiculous! They'll do
you no more harm than any of the miners here in camp!"

"Maybe so. I'm taking no chances."

Tony stormed out of the tent, trying to control the
anger that welled so readily to the surface. He looked
again at the mountains surrounding Klutina, picturing
them as a prison, holding him back from the Tanana gold
fields. "I'm going," he said to himself. "I'm going if I have
to walk!"

He spent the rest of the day bargaining for gear that
he would want to carry on the long trek overland. He
trudged back to the shack at the sawmill determined to
get a full night's sleep before starting out. Eight other
men had jammed bunks into the shack, bringing the total
to twelve. When Tony sat down to write a letter home

he could barely find a clear space on which to lay the paper.

"Dear Herb," he wrote to his younger brother, "I'm heading inland tomorrow morning. Nothing's going to stop me this time. Spent nearly all my money for a knapsack, boots, canvas coat, trousers, heavy underwear and blankets. Boy, I thought the prices were high in Seattle and Valdez! You should see what the prices are here! Astronomical, as the professor would say. After buying provisions and a rifle, I'm down to my last dollar. But I figure I won't need money if I can just get into the gold fields and start digging."

Several of the bearded men watched enviously as Tony wrote his letter. When he had finished, someone slid a crumpled old newspaper across the little table.

"Think maybe you want to read something for us, Tony?"

They listened attentively to the clear young voice reading news items that were three and four months old. One miner furtively slid a worn letter across to Tony and asked that he read the contents in a low voice that could not be overheard by others. Feeling like a priest in the confessional, Tony complied. Late in the night, when most of the others had gone to sleep, Jim Harris, a bearded veteran of Dawson and Nome, came close to the flickering candle where Tony sat. "Looking for somebody who might write a letter for me. My wife and two children back in Minnesota will be kind of wondering. . . ." He pushed a pencil and a soiled piece of paper before Tony. "Do you think you could?"

"Sure. Go ahead and start talking, and I'll start writing."

"Dear Wife," the miner said, "it's coming close to winter's end here in Klutina City. I sent you forty dollars from Valdez what I made packing over the trail, but in this prospecting business money is slow, mostly going out instead of coming in. Your socks keep my feet warm, because it's rare cold here at nights. I send my love to my daughters. Yours respectfully, your husband, Jim."

When Tony had sealed and addressed the letter, he shoved it back across the table to Harris.

The prospector fumbled in his coin purse. "Want to pay you for your trouble."

Tony shook his head and rose from the table. "No. I'll write your letters or read your mail, any time. And there'll be no charge."

Jim Harris shook his head in wonder. "You won't get far, son. This country's mighty expensive to live in."

Tony shrugged his shoulders. "We'll see."

He went outside and stood under the pale yellow disk of the moon, looking to the blue-black outlines of the mountains silhouetted in the sky. He was churning with restlessness. Harris, letter in his hand, shuffled by. "Jim," Tony asked, "is it possible to go overland to the Tanana River?"

Jim rubbed his chin reflectively. "I've heard tell of it being done. Two fellows went through last summer, and one of them made it all right. Never did find the other one. . . . Broke his leg scrambling over the country beyond the mountains. His partner went on ahead to get help. When he got some people back there, this fellow with the broken leg, he was just gone. Disappeared. Mind you," he ended hastily, "that's just a story. Something I heard."

"I don't care," Tony said explosively. "I'm going across anyhow. I'm not going to wait around with a bunch of old men—" He stopped abruptly. "I mean, I packed across the trail from Valdez. I can find my way through to the Tanana Valley."

He spun about and headed for the shack, intending to get his gear together without delay. Suddenly he raised his hand to his cheek, and looked upward to the blackened sky.

Behind him, Jim snorted, "It's snowing," he said in great disgust. "Doggone, it's snowing! Old man winter is sure hanging around."

For the first time since arriving in Alaska, Tony felt a shiver of apprehension. He had read of the dangers on the trail when the temperatures sagged to fifty or sixty degrees below zero.

And now he was going out, alone.

He wondered if he would survive.

CHAPTER SEVEN

The storm that followed was no gentle zephyr from the southern skies. Stretched out on his bunk, listening to the shrieking wind that drove the snow in a steady curtain before it, Tony thought of the Indian chief, Goodlata, and his people on the trail to Valdez. He wondered if they had reached shelter, or if, by some chance, Indians through long years of hardship had become inured to cold and suffering. But, remembering the time he had packed over the trail, coming through Thompson Pass, he knew there was no human being who could face into the wind and survive.

All through the night the wind tore at the little wooden shack. Twice Tony got up and shoved old rags under the gaping space beneath the door, trying to keep out the vicious fingers of cold. He started in surprise at the heaps of snow that had sifted inside. Once a burst of wind rushed down the tin chimney. The accumulated pressure crashed open the door of the stove and sent a shower of sparks flying across the crowded shack.

There were muffled exclamations of alarm, bare feet

dangling over bunks, and a concerted leap to beat out the glowing coals.

"Lost the fire for good," Tony said. "I'll build another."

"No use," one of the others called. "Wind'll blow it out as fast as you fix it. Just have to shiver it out until the morning."

In the dim, fluttering light of the candle that was left burning, Tony could see the white hoarfrost in the cracks of the siding creep gradually lower. It whitened in a widening river, and grew thicker with each passing minute. He could feel the cold reaching under his blankets. He wondered uneasily how he would fare when he ventured out on the trail in the morning. For he was still fiercely determined to push onward.

In the morning the blizzard was still howling, tracing a direct course from the Tazlina Glacier, carrying with it all the fury that had been pent up since the start of winter five months before.

He opened the door, his shoulder braced to take the full force of the wind. A mound of snow was heaped against the shack. Tony slammed the door shut. "We won't be going far for breakfast," he called to the men still huddled under blankets. "Let's take stock."

A few crusts of bread were pulled into the open, a dented can of peaches, and a well-chewed ham bone. In the far corner, a bright-eyed newcomer proferred a can of sour dough. The twelve men gathered around the booty. Tony burst into laughter. "We're starving to death! Let's get out of here and hunt some food!"

Suddenly he stopped. He remembered the supplies he had crammed into his pack. Without another word he walked to his bunk, yanked out the knapsack and dumped the supplies. He stacked them on the crude table. "We'll eat for a while."

One of the men cleared his throat as he reached out for the slab of bacon. "We'll make it up to you, Tony. First pack train in from Valdez. Promise."

For another hour Tony sat on his bunk, listening to the howling of the wind, and the thin, skipping sound of the snow as it brushed against the wooden sides of the shack. So crowded were the men that they were forced to move sideways as they walked in the narrow openings between the bunks. The fire had been started again, and as the heat increased, the white hoar frost retreated along the wooden walls almost as though it were alive and afraid of the warmth. There was a continual rumble of interchanging voices, some of them showing a growing irritation with the close confinement caused by the storm.

"Dang bust it," one of the men snarled, "ever I get out of this trap, I'm heading back to Valdez and climbing aboard a ship for the States. Life's just too dad-blasted short to spend looking up at a snowbank for nine months of the year. Didn't know how well off I was back in the hardware business."

"Cold? Man, I thought it was cold back in North Dakota," another snapped, "but this takes the cake. Ever I get back to the farm again, I'm going to curl up with that plow and just stay put the rest of my life."

"Come up to God's country," another whined, "and I get shoved into a room smaller'n a coffin, choking, can't breathe, can't walk, can't sit, can't sleep. I'm getting out of this country, I tell you. I'm getting out."

Listening to the endless stream of complaints, Tony was suddenly overcome with anger. He leaped to his feet, opened his mouth, then caught himself. He sat down on the bunk, fighting back the words that were storming to his lips. Afterwards, when he was calmer, he grinned to himself. "If I feel this way after one day—how'll it be after a week?"

He slipped into his heavy jacket, pulled open the door and clambered over the snowdrift. "Slam the door shut," he called over his shoulder. "I won't be back."

"Dang it, young fellow," a voice came drifting up querulously, "you come back here and shovel out this snow."

"Bring us some grub!" another called.

Tony didn't pay any attention. He dug his head down into his shoulder, bent far over, and faced into the wind. He wanted to fight his way anywhere beyond the crowded, quarreling men who were jammed inside the shack. He headed into the wind, floundering through the big drifts of swirling snow.

The tents of Mosquito Avenue were pushed in, stretched tight with the force of the storm. Stovepipes had been ripped out and stuck up ludicrously from snowbanks. One tent had burned, the black remnants etched sharply against the pure white of the new landscape.

Farther down the disappearing street, Tony saw a figure clawing wildly in the air. "Jess! Jess!" he yelled, "what is it?"

"Dang tent's blowing away! Give a hand!"

Tony waded through the drifts and grabbed tight to the cold-stiffened ropes on which Jess Morton was hauling. The wind bellied under the dirty white canvas, lifted it dangerously, then subsided for just a moment. In that time Jess Morton tumbled into the snow, and Tony, using all his strength, was able to whip the guy rope around the pin lodged into the frozen ground.

Jess struggled to his feet. "Let's get out of here!" he yelled.

Tony grabbed at Morton's shoulder as he went by. "These Indian people," he yelled, "they're caught out in this storm! Must be somewhere down by Stewart Creek! We've got to get help to them!"

Jess brushed the snow from his eyebrows, leaned close and screamed in Tony's ear, "You're too late! Come on inside!"

"Jess!" Tony pulled vigorously on the smaller man, who pulled just as vigorously the other way, toward the shelter of the tent. "You can't let them freeze to death out on the trail!"

"For heaven's sakes, boy, let me go before *I* freeze! Come inside, I say!"

They tumbled inside the tent, and slammed the door shut. Jess blew on his hands, then turned and waved toward the tables. Each one was crammed with muffled figures. A little head lifted, and a pair of big black eyes peered out at Tony. "There's your danged Indians," Jess said. "They got more sense than you think. When the storm blew up last night, they turned around and headed for shelter—and you might know they would knock on my door."

Chief Goodlata stood behind Jess, towering over the smaller man like a gigantic statue. "We will not forget," he said. "We look on you as friend."

"Friend, my foot," Jess snapped. "You'll look on me for a free meal, too, I bet you. Well," he said resignedly, "wake 'em up, and see if they can swallow some cold cornmeal mush. That's the menu for the morning. Can't keep no fire in this wind."

The storm raged for another day then stopped as suddenly as it had started. But the temperatures sagged lower and lower, and the crowded, uncomfortable gold seekers huddled about roaring stoves, quarrelsome and irritable. Only Jess Morton was cheerful. "Them Indians slipped away last night," he said to Tony. He fished behind the table he was repairing and brought out a pair of snowshoes. "Chief Goodlata said these were for you. The big fellow kind of took a shine to you."

When he went out into the snow-packed street to try on the snowshoes, Tony saw Doctor Mettinger's head bobbing from the tent office. "Found two more dead men outside their tent last night," the doctor called matter-of-factly. "They get to drinking, go outside in the cold—and that's the end of them."

That winter of 1905 was one of the coldest recorded in the Copper River country. The tight knot of men waiting at the head of frozen Klutina Lake were virtual prisoners of the sagging temperatures. Watching the antics of the men crowded about him, Tony was dismayed. Neophyte gold seekers turned easily to drink to forget the dangers and hardships that surrounded them.

Doctor Mettinger was the busiest man in camp. Each morning an allotment of corpses was discovered, the bodies frozen rigidly into the shapes assumed in the last moments when the incautious ones were drifting off to death.

And always there was the impatient straining to be

gone over the mountains into the Tanana Valley. Only the terrifying low temperatures kept the men chained to the comparative safety of Klutina City.

"Something doesn't happen soon," Doctor Mettinger observed, "this camp will just disappear."

But there was no break in the temperature. Each morning, desiring to escape as soon as possible from the quarreling men crowded into the tiny shack, Tony went outdoors and looked at the thermometer Jess Morton had hung in an inverted cheesebox. Day after day, the red mercury hung inside the bulb, unable to creep higher and record the beginning temperatures of forty below zero on the long column.

There was a wild yell from the tent at the far end of snowbound Mosquito Avenue. "New strike up on Little Delta! Walt Cooley just came through! Gold! Gold thicker'n the dust on the Dakota plains! Little Delta! New strike!"

CHAPTER EIGHT

∧∧∧∧∧∧∧∧∧∧∧∧∧∧∧∧∧∧∧∧∧∧∧∧∧∧∧∧∧∧∧∧∧∧

The camp, which had been deep in sullen lethargy, suddenly became electric with excitement. Disregarding the terrifying cold that still gripped the winter-bound settlement, the gold seekers rushed to greet the gaunt bearded man who had just stumbled into Klutina City from the north. The newcomer, Walt Cooley, huddled over a steaming mug of coffee, trying to answer the scores of questions shot at him by the men crowded into Jess Morton's makeshift restaurant.

"Sure, I saw it," Cooley said emphatically. "I staked out twenty claims myself before she froze up tight. All up and down Little Delta River. The richest find since Pedro hit it back in '02 three years ago. I'm on my way outside, now," Cooley said positively, " to get my placer equipment lined up for next spring. This time next year I'll be a millionaire."

"Many up there yet?"

"Sure, lots. And them danged pencil miners is filing on as much as a hundred claims each—but there's still claims on the creeks ain't been filed on. Good man get up there fast and he's got it made."

Tony looked about. Almost before Cooley had finished speaking men had begun to slip out of the tent. He could hear footsteps floundering in the snow. A wild chorus of barking rose into the still air.

Jess Morton saw Tony and shook his head. "I know what you're thinking, boy. Don't do it. Don't you go out on the trail till this weather breaks a bit. I want you to be moving when I see you again—not stretched out like a corpse."

Tony tried to fight the rising excitement that was building up inside him. "I know it's sensible to wait, Jess —but who wants to be sensible after all this waiting we've been doing? Good-by." He thrust out his hand, then ducked through the flap and ran to the shack.

All about him the camp was in motion. Men were throwing together their back packs as quickly as possible, some laughing and gay, others grim-faced. One after another the yelping dog teams sped down the center of the unmarked street, heading north. Men shuffling on snowshoes, bent over under heavy packs, took off into the gray light of the winter day.

The rush was on.

When Tony finally headed north, shuffling along at a steady pace on his snowshoes, the thin line of men had stretched out. Some of them had vanished into the gray gloom that marked the outer horizon; others were immediately ahead and just behind him. Instead of grouping together for mutual aid in the plunge northward into the white wilderness, the stampeders had a tendency to widen the spacing between themselves, almost as though the distrusted each other and wanted only to be alone.

Always gregarious and anxious for companionship, Tony tried twice to draw abreast of the men plodding along the unmarked trail. Each time he was rebuffed, while the gold seekers shuffled faster or pulled to one side. Little Delta was three hundred miles away, yet in the rush and urgency, the gold seekers acted as though it were just over the mountain looming before them. Tony laughed at the aloofness. It was another indication of the twisted thinking of the men who had come to Alaska.

For the third time Tony quickened his pace, trying to overtake a heavily burdened figure just ahead of him. But the bearded man, looking over his shoulder, seemed to take fright at the appearance of Tony. He veered quickly to the right, disappearing behind a clump of snow-bowed alders. Tony shrugged his shoulders. "Mighty unpopular place for a man to be alive," he said. He remembered a short cut he had seen when exploring beyond Klutina City. There was a chance that he could save three miles if he were to use it, for it connected with the river below the gorge. He turned to the left, quickened his pace, and weaved a path through the undergrowth that was heavy on the banks of the river.

In the excitement of the sudden departure, he had paid little attention to the cold. Now as he shuffled along, he became aware of the drop in temperature. The air was deathly still. Even the rabbits and snow owls that had been so plentiful had disappeared, driven to shelter by the plummeting cold. When he sucked in his breath, the cold became like a liquid, forcing a path down his windpipe, burning and searing at his lungs.

He was comfortable as long as he kept moving. When he stopped for a moment to rest, it was as though an unseen wall pressed in on him. There was a sudden, sharp sound, and he spun about, startled. Nothing was in sight save a line of gaunt birch trees. Even as he watched, there was another pop of sound, and one of the birch trees trembled. Looking closer he could see where the trees had cracked and split because of the terrifying cold.

He became wary, mindful of Chief Goodlata's words that extreme cold on the trail could kill a man quickly. He kept rubbing his hand over the tip of his nose, and along his cheek bones, wary of the numb sensation that would foretell frostbite. He wiggled his toes inside his boots, checking the circulation.

At noon he stopped to rest and prepare a hot drink. He was startled when the water he tossed to one side froze in a solid sheet in mid-air, and clattered tinnily to the ground. When he withdrew his hands from his gloves, the cold seemed to leap forward and grasp his unprotected fingers in an iron grip. He reached under his armpit and brought out the piece of meat he had stored there. He chewed on it nervously, conscious always of the cold that seemed to be a living thing, trying to gain entrance to his body.

He shuffled out quickly on his journey again, looking over his shoulder, as though expecting a sudden rush of invisible forms. He almost regretted leaving the main trail, for he was lonesome and frightened. He pondered the fate of men who were hurt or ill, helpless on the trail when the cold was so frightful.

The short day was coming to an end, the night was

heralded by lowering gray clouds that blackened out the colored sky in the west. He began to speculate where he would stop for the night; how he would keep alive until the early dawn when he could be in motion again.

He looked ahead, and through an opening in the thin trees, he could see the flat white of the frozen river. It would be better to camp on the other side, where a thick mass of alder might furnish some shelter from the deadly cold.

He plunged out on the slick ice, confident that the forty-below cold had frozen it solid. He slipped, regained his feet, and hurried onward. He was anticipating the meal he would prepare, savoring its flavor.

His mind was already on the far bank of the river; his feet were still plodding across the frozen ice. Suddenly there was a snap and crackle. The ice swayed, buckled. Without further warning he dropped into knee-deep water, plunging through to a firmer shelf of ice beneath the false surface. He lurched wildly, pulled to one side by the heavy weight of his pack. But he managed to remain upright, keeping his hand and waist away from the water that suddenly swirled unrealistically about him. A sharp cry for help sprang to his lips, but he broke it off even before it was uttered. He was alone in the wilderness. His living or dying depended only on himself. He threw himself forward to the firm ice beyond the break. Even as his booted foot with its impeding snowshoes withdrew from the break, he could feel the icy water fasten itself on his leg, biting like sharp teeth.

For the moment he thought only of getting off the ice. The threat of drowning was real, immediate. Face downward on the ice, he knew if he plunged through again he would be held under by the weight of his pack. Because of the awkwardness of his movements, fighting the pack and the snowshoes, he would not be able to fight his way upward.

But the ice held. He rolled and tumbled and humped forward, fighting to reach the bank. He stretched upward to a low-hanging spruce bow. Even in the moment of emergency, he was conscious of the sharp cut of the frozen needles raking across his face. He pulled mightily, threw himself upward, and tumbled over onto the safety of the snow bank. As he stretched outward, breathing his thanks for his escape from the waters, he was conscious of an imperceptible movement about his feet. Looking backward over his shoulder, he could see the slime forming about his boots. As he watched, the color deepened, and the wet boots were encased in ice.

He struggled to his feet, shaking with fright. In a few minutes he knew his boots would be frozen solid, and the flesh encased would automatically follow the downward plunge of temperature and freeze. Unless he could kick off his boots, massage his wet feet, warm them, and place dry socks on them, they were slated for destruction.

"Help! Help!" The minute he yelled the words, he was sorry. "I'm crazy," he whispered to himself. "There's no one around for five miles. And what can they do for me that I can't do myself?" He looked around quickly. "I've got to get these boots off, build a fire. Make it fast, boy," he said, urging himself onward.

Instinctively he leaned over, reaching with his gloved hands for the laces on his boots. He staggered to one side, pulled by the weight of his pack. With a quick motion, he shrugged out of the pack, tossing it aside. Then he kicked off his snowshoes. His motions, instead of being precise and calculated, were fumbling, harried by increasing fright. He looked at his gloved hands, wasting precious split seconds while he tried to calm himself. Then, as though it were possible to escape the terrible cold that was beginning to attack him at every side, he stepped quickly to the left and huddled beneath a clump of jack pine while he pawed at the frozen laces on his boots.

He felt an ominous tingling at the tips of his ears. He paused for a moment to pat at his cheeks, fearful that the flesh would become frosted. When he sucked in his breath, he could feel a sharp sting and burn. There was an ache at the base of his throat. Every part of his body was vulnerable, helpless before the steady encroachment of the cold.

For the moment he forgot about his feet that were becoming encased in ice. He looked about frantically for a few twigs with which to start a fire. And he paused in his fright for just one moment to pray. He knew that death was creeping close. He ripped a handful of dried twigs from the jack pine, then slashed down heavily with his arms to break off larger pieces of wood. He mounded the twigs on the snow. He pulled the glove from his right hand, and slipped the hand inside his parka to the spot under his armpit where he kept his matches dry and secure. When he withdrew the hand, holding the match tightly within his thumb and forefinger, the cold leaped upon the two. The muscles of his fingers surrendered. They refused to answer his ridiculously simple mental command to keep tight hold of the wooden match.

One after the other, as he tried to grasp them, the matches fell from his numbed fingers into the crusted snow. Tony looked at his hand, watching his fingers begin to stiffen clumsily, as though they had been stricken with an odd disease. He realized they would freeze if he exposed them any longer to the cold. With a fumbling, jerking movement, he thrust his hands back into the gloves, holding them under his armpits, while he winced with the new pain.

He tried to shuffle his feet, and they were weighted logs. He wanted to walk, but he felt as though he were rooted to the spot. He remembered the stories told around the iron stove in the cramped shack at night, tales of horror, of men lost and frozen on the trail. He remembered the grim comments of Doctor Mettinger when the frozen corpses were carried to his tent office.

Then the fear left him. He was quite sure he was going to die. Quietly he prepared himself according to the teaching of his Catholic faith. Then his thoughts wandered off to his childhood on the farm at Palatine Bridge. Once he had gone coon-hunting in the cornfield with his younger brothers, Herbert and Roy, and the three had trailed and killed a raccoon. When they had gone back to the house, tired and dirty, Tony had emptied his shining nickel-plated Smith and Wesson revolver, snapping the catch as he held the gun in his left hand. Suddenly it went off, and the boys saw the bullet bounce from the marble top of the dresser and embed itself in the plaster of the wall.

Tony had winced, clenching his fist, as he walked out to the well. When the others found him, blood was seeping between his fists, and he was white with pain. The two younger boys harnessed the buggy and raced into town with Tony, where Doctor Meyers had cleaned the bullet wound.

Now as his life ebbed away, Tony withdrew his left hand for a moment from his glove, and looked at the middle finger. The scar was still there. He shook his head, remembering the long years of dreaming and planning that had preceded this trip to Alaska.

"And I'm still not sorry," he muttered to himself. The pain in his feet was very real. It forced tears into his eyes.

Then across the thin ice of the river, he saw a small man hobbling, a little, gnomelike figure bent over with the weight of an enormous pack. Tony straightened upright. He lifted his hand stiffly, and started to cry out. Then he remembered the surliness and suspicion of the men who hit the trail during a new rush to the gold strikes, how they wanted nothing so much as to be left alone. He was afraid to call, lest the sound of his voice would send the stranger veering off on a new course.

But he had to call, for the ice was dangerous and one more forward movement might bring the little man tumbling through the false covering into the water below.

"Wait!" he yelled, and his voice came like a croak. "The ice! Careful!"

He tried to lift his arms in warning, and there was no strength left in them. He stood, bowed forward, watching the figure silhouetted against the pure white of the snow.

CHAPTER NINE

The ice swayed and buckled. The newcomer looked warily from side to side. He raced forward before the cracking ice reached him. Then he was at the bank, scrambling upward like a little animal, while he swayed under the burden on his back. After he grunted a greeting, he looked at Tony's boot, then back to the hole in the ice that was rapidly being covered with new skim ice. With a quick movement, he tossed off his pack without speaking, and knelt in the snow to make a fire. From the depths of his parka he pulled the stump of a candle which he wedged against a rock.

Tony watched, fascinated. He could see the man wince as the intense cold bit at his fingers. And he was dismayed when the little stranger, too, was unable to grasp the match firmly in his fingers and bring it sharply across the sanded edge of the box. The match slipped to the ground, and he looked at it, then at Tony, his frost-rimmed eyebrows puckering in amazement.

Tony leaned forward to help, but he was unable to move and nearly fell. He looked over the man's shoulder, blinking his eyes. He could feel himself slumping forward, as though slipping off into warm darkness. "Please let him be able to strike the match," he whispered "Please."

He watched through drooping eyelids. When he saw what was happening, his head lifted as new hope came to him. The stranger thrust a wooden match between his blunt yellow teeth. Then he lowered his fur-capped head to a small rock he held between his gloved hands. He jerked his head with a snapping movement. The match scraped across the rock, and a pale yellow flame flared. But at that precious moment, the bearded head jerked back instinctively; the lighted match was spat outward, and the weak flame died in the snow, as the man leaped forward to rescue it.

"Try it again," Tony said, and he could not recognize his voice. It sounded like the croak of a raven.

His rescuer went through the same ritual. The flame came to life, but once again it was lost when his numbed fingers could not grasp the wooden sliver. Tony slumped backward in the snow. He was quite sure it would be impossible to light a fire, that his feet would freeze, that soon he would die.

But the other, unhurried, smiling to himself, tried for the third time. The flame flared. He grasped the match between his two clenched fists, and lowered it to the waiting candle. The waxed cord charred, glowed, and burst into strong flame. It was touched to the twigs, and the blaze leaped upward.

With the advent of the fire, everything changed. The little man slashed the laces on Tony's boots, ripped off his socks, and massaged his feet roughly. When Tony leaned forward to the fire, he cautioned him, "Easy, my friend, not too close. You would freeze one minute, burn yourself the next. The fire is good—in moderation."

"What's your name?" Tony asked as he pawed into his knapsack for dry socks.

The other did not hear, or pretended not to hear. He crouched over the fire, his hands extended to its warmth while he looked beyond Tony to the frozen ice on the river. "This is something you must be careful of in extreme cold, young man," he said slowly, as though he were instructing a classroom. "The river forms a solid sheet of ice at the very bottom, then the swift water forces its way above with only skim ice as a covering." He nodded his head wisely. "You are not the first one who has broken through. Others have lost—" he looked sharply at Tony's foot, bending closer to examine the blue markings.

"My name is Tony Dimond. What is your name?" Tony repeated.

"Your foot has been frostbitten, unfortunately. We must get you back to Klutina City. Tomorrow, the day after, if you do not attend to this foot quickly. . . ." He shrugged his shoulders, and reached for his pack. "A man without his foot would be seriously handicapped in so hard a country. Come, quickly."

"You're mistaken—look!" Tony jumped about to show that it was fine. Suddenly he made a grimace, trying to stop the stab of pain. Without any further objection, he pulled on his sock, laced his boot, and took up his pack. "I'm ready."

Before they started back across the river, the stranger held out his hand to Tony. "I am happy to make your acquaintance, Mister Dimond. You ask my name—my friends call me the Dutchman. There is no other." There was an odd glint in the eyes shaded deep within the black shaggy eyebrows.

Tony shook hands solemnly. In the few months he had been north, he had learned the futility, sometimes the danger, of probing too deeply into the personal lives of the sixty thousand gold seekers who had rushed into the northland. The great majority of them were honest, sincere people, men like himself in quest only of adventure and a chance at a quick fortune. There were others among them, criminals, murderers, fugitives from the law, men who came north to forget entirely the life that had gone before. Odd names without roots, names like the Dutchman, the Sailor, the Cowboy, Tex, Oklahoma, Bedrock, Shipwreck, were common. They were a shield, a base on which men could start anew.

Hour after hour Tony hobbled back toward Klutina City, urged on by the Dutchman. The moon was full, and they were able to retrace the crude trail made by the stampeding miners. And, as though all good fortune was on his side, the temperature began an almost imperceptible rise. It lifted one degree after another until finally the Dutchman, spitting lustily into the still air, announced, "It's not more than twenty degrees below zero."

"Almost warm," Tony agreed, and suddenly he began laughing quietly to himself. His foot was paining him. Abruptly he ended his laughter, and bit his lip fiercely while he tried to keep back the tears. He was afraid that he would lose his foot, that his dream of adventure would end in disaster.

His tears were real when he stretched out on the table in Doctor Mettinger's tent office.

"We'll save your foot, Tony," the bustling doctor announced, peering over the top of his glasses, "but you're going to lose one of those toes. And I don't have any anesthetic, either. You'll have to hang tight to the Dutchman here while I go to work."

When that hour was over, and Tony stood upright, swaying dizzily, the country had left its mark upon him. For the rest of nearly fifty years he was destined to limp across the face of Alaska.

He returned to Valdez, when he was able to travel, and, for a short time, drove a sleigh and horses for the Ed Wood Transfer Company. Among his customers was the Miller Grocery Store. Dorothea Miller, the young girl who had befriended him on his arrival in Valdez, rode the sleigh with him while he delivered groceries for her father. He was twenty-four years at the time, and she was a wisp of a girl barely turned fourteen.

Long before the deep snows of Valdez were gone Tony said good-by to Dorothea Miller and turned once more inland to Klutina City. He helped Jess Morton in the restaurant, listening to the tales of disappointment that filtered back from the Tanana Valley gold strikes.

Jess slapped a pot heavily on the stove. "Pulling up stakes soon, Tony. I see the signs. Things is just petering out up there on the Tanana. Lots of gold up there—but not for the little fellow. You figure some way to get some heavy machinery in over the mountains, you'll make a hatful of money. But no other way. I'm getting back to the coast and sniffing. Hear tell Cordova's busting wide open with a new railroad pushing back to some copper strikes. That's for me. Come spring, away I go."

Tony stood in the doorway, looking out at the tall sentinel mountains hedging in Lake Klutina. Jess came and stood by his side.

"This Copper River Valley suits me fine," Tony said. "There's four hundred miles of it—lots of it still unexplored. I'm going up and down that river, and up and down every creek. I don't care if it takes five years—I'm going to explore this Valley like no other man before me."

Jess scratched the stubble on his cheek reflectively. "You'll have lots of excitement—but not much money. Mark my words, Tony. And when you get hungry—look me up in Cordova. I'll see to it that you eat."

With the first warm winds of spring, when the ice moved from the rivers and the creeks ran high in their banks, Tony left Klutina City. Most of the tents had been struck, and only a few wind-torn cabins were silhouetted against the sky as the little settlement took on the air of a ghost town. He walked with an eager step, face lifted to the sky, a cheerful gangling young Lincoln who rarely turned back to look at the place where last he had slept.

Once again he was free, and all of Alaska was waiting. The country seemed like a vast green book, the pages of which would be turned by a forward movement. There was a breath of daring, a craving for adventure in Tony that was not easily denied. He limped slightly, but there was no stopping his movement. He remembered little of the incident when he had fallen through the ice, and never allowed himself to think of the suffering he had undergone.

The mountains were waiting to be climbed, the creeks to be forded, the rivers to be crossed. The thick spruce of the green forests in the lower levels were a challenge, seeming to invite his questing feet. The bare smooth rock above the timber line of the mountains, the lonely region of cloud and rain, were a whispering song of allurement, an enticement to climb even higher on the bare rock in an effort to touch the sky.

There were times when he moved with loud-talking, loud-singing prospectors on their way to rumored finds. When he finally encountered his friend from New York, Joe Murray, he went prospecting with him for long, enjoyable months on the Tazlina River.

"Tony," Joe Murray said to him thoughtfully, staring at him across the leaping yellow flames of the fire, "I've been chasing after gold for three years—and I think it's time I settled down. Been thinking of opening a law office, maybe in Valdez, or Cordova."

"Glad to hear it, Joe. Territory needs a good lawyer. If I hit it big and have to incorporate, I'll bring the papers to you."

Joe tossed a log on the flames. "I'd rather you were sitting alongside me in the law office, Tony. Partners."

"But, Joe—I've had no law training—well, not much. That stint in New York City a few years ago."

"You're intelligent, Tony, and—if you'll pardon my bluntness—you're a good talker. You know this country. You love it. Put them all together, add some formal training that I could help you get—and you're launched in law."

"I wish it was that easy." Tony shook his head dubiously.

"All right—it won't be that easy. But no matter how hard it is, you've got the courage to tackle it."

Tony stood up and walked uncertainly by the fire. Joe looked up at him earnestly.

"Tony," he said quietly, "do you ever have the feeling we're wasting time? Prospecting like this? Chasing over the hills? Floating down rivers?"

"Somebody's got to do it," Tony said stubbornly.

"Yes, but why us? Maybe it's conceit, Tony, but don't you think some bigger job might be waiting?"

Tony held his hands out to the fire. He grinned slowly. "You're scaring me now, Joe. I don't want a bigger job. All I want to do is to get to know this country like the back of my hand. I'm not ashamed to tell anyone I'm in love with Alaska. And I want to stay out here along the rivers, and on the mountains, back here on the creeks, close, right where I can lay my cheek down at night and touch the country. Maybe something else will come later, but right now, Joe, this is all I want." He pointed to the fire, and looked around in the darkness toward the mountain ridges gleaming faintly with their snow pockets high in the air.

When he woke in the morning, Joe Murray was gone, and he was alone.

He sketched his own maps of the country, then memorized the paths he broke in the wilderness. There were many times, he knew, when he was the first white man to tread upon some distant corner of the Copper River Valley.

Search for gold was always his prime motive, yet, he told himself ruefully, even that was secondary to his love for this new land. He spent hours each day crouched in the sun, or huddled down under the rain, a gold pan in his hands, tilted to the water of some swift-running creek, twirling with that slight, twisting, circling dip and swirl that is learned so slowly, and yet, once learned, is never forgotten. His heart knew the excited triphammering that comes as the dross is washed away, as the sand body dwindles, as the faint dull yellow of raw gold begins to creep in a sturdy line toward the uppermost lip of the gold pan.

Yet for every hour that he spent in his search for gold, he spent two on the sides of the mountains, rifle in hand, eyes alert to the first movement of game among the spruce blanket of the hills. The country was good to him. Rarely did he go hungry. He tracked brown bears across the hills, and was tracked in turn. He feasted on ptarmigan and grouse in the months of spring when the small birds swarmed upon the hills. He fashioned his own fishing rod and lifted savory trout from the icy waters.

In the summer of 1906, when the salmon were running up the river, he visited his friends, the Indians of Chief Goodlata's tribe, and sat by their fires, munching on freshly caught salmon. He sat by the river in long hours of monosyllabic conversation with the young chief, watching the turning fish wheel lifting the trapped salmon, seeing them plummet into the wooden troughs to captivity and the inevitable end of the smoke racks.

It was July when he sat on the banks of the river with the tall chief. There were more than one hundred of the tribe busy at the salmon smoking racks. When Tony returned in October, there were only forty still alive. An epidemic of smallpox had decimated the tribe.

He slept with his head pillowed on a mound of dried

spruce needles, listening to the roar of racing water leaping down from the melting glaciers that formed a complete circle from sea to sea. He washed his hands in the waters of the Chitina River, and bathed his feet in the melted ice of the Tazlina Glacier. He prospected on the gray moraine of the Copper River, and dug under the ice of the Columbia Glacier. He staked innumerable claims, going through the interminable labor of sinking a shaft to bedrock, inching galleries outward in every direction, probing for an elusive strain of gold.

He marveled at the swift turn of days, the hurrying of one season fast upon the other. Always there was something new to be seen, some new excitement to carry him forward through the day into the night, and the days beyond. At the end of each summer, when the first snows would appear upon the mountain ridges and begin the slow inexorable climb downward, drawing winter closer, he would determine to leave Alaska, if only for a brief time in order to see his mother and father, his sisters and brothers. Yet 1906 drew to a close, and still he did not quit Alaska. The next year went by, and the next, and still another, each one dropping silently and unnoticed, so engrossed was Tony in the excitement of living out the days in the last frontier.

He wrote home faithfully, keeping his family posted on his movements. And when the mail came in from the States, still damp from the long overseas voyage, he retired to a quiet spot and read the messages over and over again. Aching with homesickness, he decided to take the first boat south; then his eyes would lift to the hills, to the snow-spotted valleys of the mountains towering overhead, and he would remember one other creek that he meant to explore, one other mountain that he intended to climb. He would shoulder his pack and slip away into the wilderness.

With the coming of winter, when his supplies were exhausted, he retreated to the little mining camps in the Valley, working for wages, always with the goal of new supplies for the new year, and a new chance to plunge into the wilderness. Frequently he returned to Valdez, renewing his friendship with Joe Murray, who had opened a law office in the small town. And with each visit to Valdez he remembered to bring back some small trinket from the wilderness that would catch the eye of Dorothea Miller, rapidly maturing into a young lady.

Through the years until 1911, Tony Dimond remained in the Copper River Valley, in his own words, "Living a harum-scarum life," drifting through the mountain corridors, prospecting, trapping, sharing the restlessness that gripped all who had come upon Alaska.

The big gold strikes of the Interior country were history. Alaska had fallen from public notice. The vast majority of the sixty thousand who had surged northward had fallen back, beaten by the savagery of the country, and retreated to the warm shelter of the States two thousand miles to the south.

A few, like Tony Dimond, clung tenaciously to the land.

When he was not buried deep in the green and white wilderness of the mountain country, he worked around the copper camps as a blacksmith and laborer, swinging heavy hammers, digging ditches, and building camps from raw lumber. He spent one winter as a blacksmith

for the Michigan Corporation, adjacent to the fabulous
Kennecott Copper Mines.

The word "copper" was becoming more and more important, not only in the life of Tony Dimond, but in the
life of Alaska. Tony spent his thirtieth birthday, November 30, 1911, sitting by the banks of the swirling Canyon
Creek. He looked up at the sound of heavy voices shouting in the air, urging on a string of pack mules. The
bearded hostler at the head of the string came and
squatted by Tony's side.

"Any luck with the gold pan, friend?"

Tony shrugged his shoulder. "Nothing spectacular.
Always a little showing, but not enough to warrant a
stampede. Where you heading with the pack train?"

"Over to the foot of the Wrangell Mountains. Biggest
copper find in the history of the world. Some big eastern
millionaires bought up the whole shebang. Bringing in a
railroad from Cordova. If you're wise, son," the packer
said, "you'll get on the payroll of the Copper River and
Northwestern. More gold'n you'll ever get outta twirling
that gold pan."

That night, rolled in his blankets, he looked up at the
stars and at the white sheen of the snow glittering in the
light of the moon high on the side of Spirit Mountain.
Perhaps a few months on the railroad, in the company
of other young men—

But instead, the next morning he headed for the
glaciers and the rugged mountains of the White River
country, free as the winds that raced down the peaks.
He sat astride a great gray horse, and behind was a pack
horse laden with equipment, representing all the wealth

he had gathered in his long years of wandering through the Copper River Basin.

At the swift-flowing Nizina River, he paused to feed and water his horses. He checked his gear, tightened the straps that held his worldly possessions on the two animals, then urged them forward into the icy waters. Halfway across, the pack horse slipped and fell heavily against the animal on which Tony was riding. Both animals went down. The current tore at them viciously. They struggled, fought to their feet, then fell again in a tangle of ropes and straps.

Tony was thrown to one side. The bitterly cold water took hold of him as though it were sharp-pointed tongs. He went under, choking and gagging. His clothing pulled him deeper and deeper. He tried to hold his breath while he fought upward to the surface. But the pain and the shock overcame him, and he opened his mouth and swallowed gagging mouthfuls of water. His head struck a submerged rock. He could feel himself sinking lower, striking against the swirling sand at the bottom of the river.

CHAPTER TEN

/\

Tony knew that there was a time when he ceased struggling, when he was almost inert at the bottom of the river, his only motion supplied by the vicious tugs of the current. He did not crawl from the river; he was tossed out bodily at a sharp bend that overran a spit of sand thrust into the stream. He rolled over and over. Then he lay flat on his back. His first conscious feeling was that of the cold wind blowing across his cheek. When he began to shiver violently, the force of the motion made his eyelids flutter open. He tried to lift his head. When it fell back, he tried again. Finally he was able to roll over, lift himself, and look back to the river. The horses were gone.

He crawled higher from the reach of the waters, pulled himself upright by a small spruce tree and swayed dizzily on his feet. His face hurt, and he reached instinctively into his pocket for a bandana to touch to the bruised skin. The bandana was gone, ripped away by the raging waters. He tried each pocket in turn and found them frayed and empty, ravaged by the force of the churning waters.

He shivered violently again. The raw wind tugging at his wet clothing was a threat of pneumonia. Automatically he began to trot along the river bank, his eyes to the water, looking for the two horses.

There was nothing hidden for long in the river. A quarter of a mile down from the spot where he had crawled out to safety Tony found the two animals. They were head down in the water, drowned. The packs had been stripped from one horse, the saddle from the other.

He looked at the grotesque forms bobbing in the white-capped water, then down at his open hands. Then he looked away from the river to the bare brown of the mountain tops hemming him in like a prisoner. "Everything," he whispered to himself, "everything I own is gone."

It was six years since he had stepped from the boat at Valdez; six years of almost unrelenting effort, trying to accumulate a small share of the wealth that was promised by Alaska. He stood uncertainly in the middle of a dimly marked path by the side of the river. One way pointed to the Kennecott and the new excitement of the copper mines probing into Bonanza Mountain. The other led back to the sea, to Valdez and the steamers waiting for the return to the States.

For the first time, Tony Dimond was utterly discouraged. "I'm finished," he whispered to himself. "I'm going back. I'm through." The wind came through the spruce, echoing the words. The mountains seemed to grow darker, more forbidding. Even the river churned with a deeper, more menacing roll.

He turned away, and started down the trail.

It was cold, and he quickened his steps, trying to forget the clammy touch of his wet clothing, trying to find a new exultation in this return to the States, and the new life that would be waiting. But every step was made with an effort. He kept looking over his shoulder at the mountains that he had grown to love. He reached out his hands and touched the low-hanging spruce bows that brushed close to the trail. Everything cried out for him to stay with the country he had loved so well. "You've got to be sensible," he told himself savagely. "You've tried and you've failed."

He scrambled over a newly fallen spruce that blocked the trail, scratching himself on the sharp branches that thrust themselves at him. Suddenly he stopped and sniffed. There was the smell of wood smoke in the air. He quickened his pace, broke into a small clearing, and saw a tiny cabin on the far side. A brown and white husky came charging at him, snapping and snarling. Then the dog's attention was distracted by a lumbering porcupine, and it went charging off in cautious pursuit. Tony kept going ahead toward the wavering column of smoke coming from the cabin. He stumbled over the plowed ground underfoot. He blinked in astonishment. The high-pitched whinny of a horse lifted into the still air. From a shed on stilts came the cautious muttering of chickens.

As Tony approached, the door of the cabin swung back and a stoop-shouldered man stepped outside. He shuffled forward, his hand outstretched.

"Every time I see you, young man, you are wetter

than my dog after a swim in the river. What happened
this time?"

"Dutch!" Tony ran the last steps and grasped the outstretched hand. "I'm happy to see you! But what's this—
chickens, horses, cows—it's a farm."

"Three horses, my friend. No cow. True, I have several
chickens." The Dutchman looked proudly about at the
cleared land, at the ugly stumps still thrust upright in
the midst of the plowed ground. "This is my homestead,
on which I have filed. It is my share of Alaska, for all
time." He reached out and took Tony's arm, and tugged
toward the cabin. "But you must get inside. You are cold
and wet, as usual. We must get you into dry clothes, and
tell me, what misadventure befell you this time?"

Later, seated at a rude table made from rough-hewn
slabs, with a candle guttering eerily in the dark interior
of the cabin, the Dutchman leaned forward excitedly.
"This, my friend, is what I have done. I came on this
country looking for shelter, for a home. I intend to stay—
oh, perhaps not always here on the Nizina River—but I
intend to stay in Alaska. Until I die," he added simply.

"You're a farmer," Tony said defensively. "You know
about these things."

The Dutchman waved his hand deprecatingly. "I was
born and raised, all my life, in a big city, in—" he broke
off abruptly. "I knew nothing about farming when I
came, as you did, around the bend in the trail and saw
this flat land with not too much timber. I was hungry,
and cold, just as you were a few hours ago. But I was not
discouraged. For years I have been searching, not for
something to take, but for something to give to this

country which has been good to me. And with this land, I knew I had found what I had been searching for."

"But farming," Tony said, puzzled, "why farming? Everybody is looking for gold, for copper, coal—and," he laughed shortly, "you find some flat land and it makes you happy?"

"Do not laugh, my friend," the Dutchman said earnestly. "You are still young. Perhaps the time has not yet come for you to discover what I have discovered."

"Well," Tony said finally, rising from the table, "I don't care. I've reached the end of the line here in Alaska. I've tried for six years, and whatever I'm looking for has escaped me entirely. I've had a lot of fun and adventure." He thrust his hands deep into the pockets of the old trousers the Dutchman had supplied him. "I'm just as broke today as the morning I landed up in Valdez, six years ago. I can't go on like this. I've got to get out, go back to the States and try all over again down there."

The old man placed his hand on Tony's elbow. "Do not be discouraged, Tony. In my eyes you are still young. But if you do not learn what is necessary, you will be older even than I."

"I don't understand you," Tony said. "I'm tired." He walked past the Dutchman, opened the door, and stood outside, leaning back against the rough logs of the cabin. The dog came and sniffed curiously at the familiar boots Tony was wearing, then slipped away again into the darkness. Overhead a thin white sliver of moon was bright against the dark blue of the sky. The mountains were black jagged lines crowding the small cabin on every side. In the distance he could hear the faint murmur of the Nizina River racing downward to the sea.

"I talk too much," the Dutchman said quietly, "and it is true you are very tired. I have prepared a sleeping place for you by the fire. Come inside when you are ready."

For a long time Tony remained motionless, his face lifted to the light of the moon. From the thin, uncertain noises of the night he could trace the movement of the birds and the animals that were active under the cover of darkness. He thought of the hundreds of men he had known in these six years since coming north. He remembered the long line of adventurers who had filed from the boat in Valdez, each one certain of victory over the unknown country of Alaska. Now most of them were gone. Only a few, like himself, had clung tenaciously to the land.

And even these had been conquered, one by one, until it seemed he stood alone.

There was Jack Crandall who had spent one winter too many alone in a crude lean-to on the banks of Dewey Creek, waiting for the coming of the spring when he could work the pile of crushed rock and gravel he had heaped on the banks of the creek. He had sat in his lean-to—huddled by a fire, looking at the crushed rock, and speculating on the wealth it would bring. The cold had crept upon him unsuspecting, and he had died as he sat, arms outstretched to a fire that had failed him during a night of sub-zero weather.

He remembered Jess Morton who had prospered with his restaurant in the new town of Cordova, until the day he had stepped triumphantly upon the steamer that was to take him and his wealth back to Seattle. Before the boat was out of sight it had struck a rock, and Jess and all his wealth had been swallowed by the waters of Prince William Sound.

There was Ted Jorgenson, younger than Tony, gayer than any man who had pierced the Copper River Valley, quick to a song, or a gay tale that would send a camp rocking in laughter. He had gone out on the trail, on another will-o-the-wisp that had men in constant motion, and somewhere the cold had overtaken him, and he had faltered. The wolves that had been waiting swarmed in, and there was little left to mark the end of a great adventure.

Each in turn had come north to live his dream, to fight his own fight with the country. Most had fled, a few had stood and resolved not to give ground. All of them had faced slow disintegration that led through a fuzzy span of years and endless wandering. Tony knew that those caught in the backwash, as Alaska slowly slipped from public notice, considered themselves the conquerors, yet, in reality, they were the vanquished, and the land, the whole sweep of Alaska, was the true victor.

He could scarcely count on the fingers of one hand the men who had looked upon Alaska differently, who cast their lot with the Territory, who called Alaska home. Dorothea Miller's father, the grocer down in Valdez, was one of them. Joe Murray, his partner on many a wilderness jaunt and now a lawyer in Valdez, was another. The Dutchman was the best example of all, a man who lifted the soil of Alaska, and let it sift through his fingers, uttering the words that bring a depth of understanding few men ever come to realize. "This is mine. This is my land."

Tony stepped further out into the clearing, and the

dog came from the shadows and moved in slow circles about him.

He had to make his decision. This night. Would he join the hordes who had swarmed upon the land, and then retreated, or would he cast his lot with those few who had made Alaska a home?

He held his clenched hands before him, and looked up at the mountains looming overhead.

"I've started with nothing but these hands before," Tony whispered to himself. "I can do it again. I can't give up this country. I won't."

He knelt on the ground and placed his arm around the neck of the big dog that stood by him. He touched his hand to the cold earth. In that gesture was his promise that his life and that of Alaska would be one. He turned, walked to the cabin, and threw back the door. "Dutch!" he called.

The little man was sitting on the side of his bunk, a worn, tattered Bible on his knees. The lone candle had been moved thriftily to the wooden box by the bunk, and Dutch was reading carefully, his moving lips spurred on by the index finger that traveled across the closely spaced print. He looked up at Tony.

"Yes?"

"I wanted to tell you—I'm staying. I'm not going to quit."

The old man nodded. "I know. We will talk about it in the morning." He turned back to his reading.

But the next morning, when the two were making plans, the dog outside the cabin suddenly leaped into action, tearing down the trail to run headlong into a horse that was floundering on the muddy trail. The

Dutchman ran out and retrieved the dog; the horse raced into the clearing, and Joe Stanton, the mail carrier, wiped the perspiration from his face. "Dang weather," he snapped, "can't make up its mind to freeze a man to death or let him drown in his own sweat."

"You will stay for breakfast?" the Dutchman asked. "We see you only once each month."

"Ain't no one to refuse a meal. Be glad to pull up a chair." Stanton dug into his mail pouch, sorted through a half dozen letters, and handed one to the Dutchman. "Looks like you're in for a little trip yourself."

Tony saw the Dutchman tremble slightly as he reached for the letter. He tore it open, read it slowly, then looked doubtfully at Tony. "I am summoned to serve as a juror in the court in Valdez. I will be gone six weeks." His eyes dimmed. "It is three years since I have been in the city."

"City, huh!" Stanton snorted. "Lucky if there's five hundred people left in Valdez. Everybody's gone over to Cordova and the danged railroad."

"You go ahead and enjoy yourself, Dutch," Tony insisted. "I'll take care of things here."

So Tony waited out the days, making frequent trips around the trap line. He was anxious for the return of the Dutchman, for the time when the two might set out in search of a new homestead for Tony. But as the days lengthened, and the supplies dwindled, he decided to ride into the new copper mining center at Kennecott, near the head of the new railroad coming up one hundred and thirty-one miles from Cordova. He rode one horse and led another.

Kennecott, dominated by the sprawling red mill on one side of the mountain, was a sea of strangers im-

ported to work in the mine. Tony gazed uneasily at the
aerial tramways running far overhead from the mill to
the mines four miles distant. He kept repeating to himself the words of the Dutchman, "Do not think only
what you can rip from the land—see what you can offer
to make it a better place to live in." The riches of Alaska
were being robbed, hurried down to the seacoast, and
sent off to the States. There was nothing left behind but
miles of empty tunnels.

He was glad to be gone with the supplies, heading out
to the wilderness again, toward the Dutchman's homestead and the Chitina Valley, the greatest scenic splendor
in Alaska.

He urged his horse forward, along the trail that followed the eastern shoulder of the Kennecott Glacier,
fording the innumerable streams that came in a spring
freshet from the mountain of ice. He negotiated the
Nizina River carefully, remembering his experience of
the previous fall when he had lost everything he owned.

With the river safely crossed, he urged his horses
forward at greater speed. As usual, he was hungry, and
already he was planning the meal he would place upon
the table on his return to the cabin. He talked aloud to
himself—and to the horses—shouted and sang, and
listened to the echoes bouncing from the mountain cliffs.
He appreciated the beauty of towering peaks, more
beautiful, perhaps, than any other in all the Territory
of Alaska. On every side, as far as he could see, snow-
tipped peaks ringed the horizon. In the pockets of the
mountains were vast fields of ice, and below, stronger
than them all, were the Nizina and Chitina and Copper

Rivers, carving their own paths through the maze of mountains.

He had his Colt in hand, and he fired enthusiastically at any likely target. He ducked low under spruce limbs heavy with the spring rains. Crossing Young Creek, he saw a bright rock shining high on the cliffside, bright in the late afternoon sun. He aimed his .45, ready to fire.

At that moment a wolverine leaped across the trail. Tony's horse bolted in terror. He was thrown from the saddle. His right foot caught in the stirrup, and he was dragged head down along the trail. When he made a wild lunge to right himself, the gun fired. He felt a sickening pain as the bullet ripped through his thigh.

The shot added to the terror of the horse, and it galloped wildly away, tearing Tony's foot from the stirrup. He crumpled in a heap on the trail.

CHAPTER ELEVEN

ΛΛΛΛΛΛΛΛΛΛΛΛΛΛΛΛΛΛΛΛΛΛΛΛΛΛΛΛΛΛΛΛΛ

The pain was so violent that Tony fainted. The blood streaming from his leg saturated the spruce needles covering the ground.

He was aroused by the querulous call of a wolf pack debating the coming forays of the night. He was flat on his back in the middle of the trail. Overhead the canopy of spruce formed a curtain that was shutting out the sky. He pulled himself up on one elbow, wincing at the pain in his leg. Far down the trail he could see the rays of the sun glinting on the metal of the Colt .45. There was nothing that he wanted more than the feel of the Colt in his hand. He turned over painfully on his chest, dug his elbows and one knee into the ground for leverage, and inched along the trail.

He had as his goal the almost invisible speck of metal. "I've got to get it," he whispered to himself. "I've got to get it." He thought of the horses. They had vanished, pounding on the path that led to the Dutchman's homestead. "Even if they were here," Tony muttered to himself, "I couldn't get aboard. This leg's hurting too much."

He tried to be calm as he pulled himself laboriously on the sliding carpet of dried spruce needles. Defense against the wolf packs was the first essential. He was numbly curious about his wound, yet he would not surrender to the curiosity. He continued the labored movement, inching toward the gun.

The howling of the wolves came louder. In his six years in the wilderness he had learned their habits. They circled endlessly, in a continual debate, keeping a ceaseless pressure on the intended victim. But a ready weapon, a bright fire, and vigilance was an effective barrier. "I've almost got the gun," Tony whispered, as he gained another foot along the trail. "Next the fire." He did not add the third requisite—vigilance, for he could feel himself growing weaker. And his thoughts began to stray from the Colt lying ahead, to the increasing pain in his thigh. The desire to stop, to examine the wound, to try and quench the flow of blood, became a clamoring shout within him. It was only when he saw the gray shadows of the wolves slipping through the timber on either side of the trail, that he was able to stifle the inward clamor, and continue onward to his objective.

The space between him and the gun narrowed. His fingers were outstretched, grasping, when very quietly the gun began to dance in slow, rhythmic motion. Its sharp outline dulled.

For three hours Tony was stretched almost lifeless on the trail. He was delirious, dreaming of his home in New York.

The jingling sound of bells and the thudding of a horse's hoofs on the soft, cushioned ground aroused him.

He was able to feel the vibration where the palms of his hands touched the spruce needles. He jerked himself upright, disregarding the pain, and looked down the trail. He managed to twist his face in a smile, and lift his hand in greeting. "Hi, Joe," he called weakly. "What's in the mailbags for me?"

"Tony! What happened? What's wrong?" Joe Stanton swung down from his horse and hurried to Tony's side. "What's going on here?" He touched his hand to Tony's blood-stained trousers. "Somebody take a shot at you?"

"Yes, me." Quickly Tony gasped out the story of the accident.

Stanton slashed at Tony's trousers with his knife. He whistled in astonishment when he looked at the wound. "Didn't waste any time, that bullet," he said briskly. "Just took a trip from the top of your thigh here, and came on out above the knee. All you got is the hole." He reached into his saddle bags for bandages.

"I've got that to be thankful for," Tony said. There was more that he wanted to say, but the pain was becoming intense and he found it almost impossible to bring his thoughts together in coherent sentences.

Stanton finished bandaging the wound. He called his horse close by, then put his arm about Tony and started to lift him. "Get you aboard," he grunted, "and we'll walk real easy into Kennecott. Doctor there will. . . ."

"Joe."

"What is it?"

"Don't move me. I'd rather stay here." Tony bit his lip. "I can't. . . ."

Stanton eased Tony down to the ground. He looked about, perplexed. "Guess you know best. I'll ride like the wind into Kennecott and bring out help; something to carry you easy on."

"Joe—the gun." Tony motioned.

"Yeah, that's right." He placed the gun firmly in Tony's outstretched hand. Then he went to his saddle-gabs, dug deeply, and came up with a tin coffeepot. He ran down the trail and dipped the pot into a stream of clear water. He placed it close by Tony.

"Drinking water," he said.

"Thank you."

"I'll get going. Now don't you worry none, Tony. Ain't but twenty-eight miles into Kennecott, and I'm the man who knows how to make old Jed here really step out. You just hang on. We'll be back before you even miss us."

He leaped on his horse and thundered down the trail.

Tony watched the mail carrier vanish around a bend. He reached for a twig and scratched a line in the soil where the shadow of a spruce branch was resting. Then, with the revolver gripped firmly in his hand, his shoulders propped against a fallen log, he started his lonely vigil.

The darkness was almost complete when far in the distance he heard a dim rhythmic pounding, a confused rumble of sound that reminded him of the night noises made by the freight trains of the New York Central on the sweeping curves beyond Amsterdam in his home state. He was drifting off in a dull reverie of the scenes of his childhood when the noise became louder and more insistent. Suddenly a voice was lifted in a loud hail.

Tony forced himself to his elbows. He wanted to lift a hand, to shout a greeting. He could feel the warm flow of tears on his cheeks.

A hundred yards away horses stopped. Tony could hear the quiet monotone of voices.

"It was right here, I left him," he heard Stanton saying. "Right here."

"Must've crawled off into the timber to die," another said matter-of-factly.

"Maybe we ought to make camp and look for him in the morning," another voice said. "In darkness like this, a man could get hurt looking for a body."

At the thought of being left alone, Tony strained with all his might to shout, but still the muscles in his jaw refused to respond. In desperation he lifted his gun, pointed it in the air, and fired.

It was then they found him.

The spring of 1912 burst over Alaska with a tremendous surge while Tony Dimond fought for his life in a Cordova hospital.

In the year that followed his accidental shooting he was to undergo seven operations. He grew to accept the accompanying pain with a resignation that befitted the making of a hero. Best of all, in the interminable days and weeks and months of patient waiting, he refused to surrender his one dream, the dedication of his life to Alaska.

Propped upright in the hospital bed, he looked through the window toward the mountains that stood like tireless soldiers in the long sweep of Prince William Sound. In his mind, he walked from the bed that held him prisoner and strode again the wilderness trail of the Copper River Basin.

There was an endless stream of visitors who came to his room. In his years of prospecting through the valley the tall young schoolteacher from New York had made many friends. The Dutchman appeared, shaking his head in bewilderment at the sudden tragedy that had overtaken Tony.

"So soon as you get well, we hit the trail and pick for you a homestead. One year from now you have your own chickens, your own horses—everything! Yesterday," Dutch continued excitedly, " a boat came from the Kenai Peninsula. I saw potatoes grown there—this big!" He bulged out his cupped hands to illustrate.

"Sure, Dutch. Sure."

Doctor Schrock, who had tended his wound in Kennecott, stopped by when he was in Cordova.

"We've had a lot of drifters, Tony, you know that. Here today and gone tomorrow. We've had a few like the Dutchman—honest, hard-working people anxious to sink roots in the country. There's only a handful of educated men like yourself, Tony, men with a background we could use. We need schoolteachers. We need more doctors. We need lawyers. You could be any one of the three."

One of his visitors, a gray-haired man, brought him a book. "Doctor Schrock asked me to stop by and introduce myself. I'm Tom Donohoe. Don't suppose you've ever heard of me; I have a law office over in Valdez."

Tony held out his hand. "One of my partners when I was prospecting on the Tazlina River was Joe Murray. He was a lawyer. We used to talk about law, sitting around the fire at night, listening to the winds blow." He stroked his chin reflectively. "The summer before I came north, I worked a few months in a law office in New York City. Fascinating."

Donohoe nodded his head. "Guess that's what Doctor Schrock had in mind."

"What do you mean?"

"He thinks you'd make a good lawyer. Thinks, too, the two of us might make quite a team over in Valdez."

Tony's mouth sagged open. "He said that?"

"Un-huh."

Tony sat upright. "While I'm laid up here, I'll think about it. How would I start?"

Donohoe reached behind his back, grasped the thick book in his hand, and tossed it on the bed. "Start reading."

Tony fingered the book. *An Introduction to Law— Zehtner.*

From that day on Tony read every law book that he could uncover in the small town of Cordova. He wrote frequently to Tom Donohoe over in Valdez telling of his progress, asking for more books to study. Back came encouraging notes and suggestions for further reading.

"It's not easy," Tony admitted to Doctor Council in the long chats the two had, "but it's keeping my mind off this leg. I figure, if you doctors keep chipping away long enough at that bone, I'll be a full-fledged lawyer!"

Doctor Council nodded. "I'd like to tell you, Tony, that we're nearly finished, but I can't." He rose ponderously to his feet and looked out to the mountains and sea. "You've been here two months. It will be another six months and more operations before we're sure that leg of yours will be saved. If studying law will help you pull through, keep at it."

And Tony Dimond did. Leaning to one side to overcome the continual pain in his injured leg, he outlined a course of study and applied himself to it relentlessly. In addition to law books, he read all that he could about the history of the Territory of Alaska, and particularly of the slow-moving relations between the Congress of the United States and the neglected Territory.

Late one night in May, 1912, when the light of the lost day was still a ghostly white on Mount Steller, he heard the sound of quarreling voices in the street, the pounding of footsteps on the wooden sidewalks, and the hoarse cry of men calling to each other in anger. He threw back the covers and dragged himself to the open window which looked down toward the waterfront. Men were rushing down the street, shovels swinging from their hands.

In the gray gloom Tony could see a ship tied to the wharf. The onrushers grouped closer as they reached the ship. As he watched, a few daring ones leaped from the wooden wharf over the rail of the heavily burdened vessel. There was a clang of steel on steel, then white, darting spots of foam as something repeatedly struck the water.

"Hey, you," Tony yelled out the window. "What is it? What's going on?"

"The coal ship! They're dumping the coal ship into the bay! Come on down and join the fun!"

"Coal ship?" Tony repeated the question to himself. How long had he been sick he asked himself? What was happening to Alaska?

When the nurse came in she was horrified to see Tony by the window. "Back into bed with you, Anthony Dimond! We spend day and night trying to keep you alive—and here you're trying to jump out the window! Back—before I tell the Doctor!"

"Nurse," he asked, "what is it? What's all the excitement?"

"Ah!" she snorted while she smoothed the covers. "Those crazy men. They'll do anything for excitement. A shipment of coal came in from the States, and they don't like it. They think we should be using Alaskan coal. And what do they do?" she asked dramatically. "They go aboard that ship just like it was the Boston Tea Party and they dump the coal overboard! What a waste!"

When Doctor Council came in he confirmed the story. "It's symptomatic of the Territory, Tony. It's sick just as you've been sick. Here we are perhaps the richest land in the world, yet we're going backwards. Imagine the foolishness of bringing in coal when we have millions of tons of it right in the Territory that the Federal Government won't let us mine. I tell you, Alaska must do something. It must find a leader, a man who will tell those people back in Washington, D. C. just what's wrong up here, what we need to develop this north country the way it should be." He probed the wound still open on Tony's thigh. "To put it bluntly, what we need is a politician—a good one."

Tony bit his lip to keep from gasping with pain.

There was a day of grief when word came of the Dutchman. The old man had been found in his cabin, sitting rigid in death, with the pages of his worn Bible fluttering in the wind that came through the opened door.

For the balance of his stay in the hospital, Tony studied without ceasing. Finally he said good-by to Doctor Council, Doctor Schrock, and Doctor Chase, the three men who had saved his leg from amputation—and to the nurses who had grown to respect and admire him for his fortitude. He said good-by to the other patients with whom he had spent many long hours reading aloud in a typical gesture of kindliness that was second nature to him. Then, white and thin, he walked out of the hospital, and down the plank sidewalks to the wooden dock where a ship was waiting.

The vessel carried him to Valdez to the same wharf where he had come ashore in Alaska more than seven years before. Tom Donohoe was there to greet him, and as they walked slowly up the plank sidewalk of McKinley Street, Tony noted the changes that had come over the town since his last visit. He was attracted to a young lady standing on the other side of the street.

He forced his way across the street and held out his hand to Dorothea Miller. "I want to thank you for the letters you wrote while I was in the hospital," he said simply. "Many little things helped me make up my mind to get better fast. Your writing was one of them."

"I'm happy you're going to remain in Valdez, Tony. Mother hopes you'll call often—if your law studies will permit."

"I intend to call—often." He bowed slightly and rejoined Tom Donohoe. "Let's take a look at that law library of yours, Tom."

"Wait a minute. You come out of the wilderness, out of the hospital, fresh new into town—and sweep up the Mayor's daughter—what's going on here?"

"Nothing. You're looking at a man with five dollars in his pocket and a big hospital bill hanging over his head. Put out of your mind any ideas that might be floating around in there!"

While Tony regained his strength, he clerked in Tom Donohoe's law office, a small wooden building on Reservation Avenue just across the street from the Courthouse.

The day finally came when he took his bar examination under the guidance of Tom Donohoe.

On January 1, 1913, Anthony Joseph Dimond was admitted to the practise of law in the Territory of Alaska. He was thirty-two years old.

Afterwards, limping slightly, with his head lifted proudly, he walked along the wagon road that led north to Fairbanks. The snow was deep, but he walked in the firmly packed ruts, his eyes lifted to the mountains and glaciers on every side. He stood on the long bridge that crossed the frozen gravel flats. The wind raced from the gigantic Columbia Glacier, over Anderson Glacier, picking up strength as it dipped through the ice gullies of Shoup Glacier. But Tony was not conscious of the cold. He raised his eyes to the moon-touched peaks of the Chugach Mountains and the Wrangell Mountains.

He wanted to reach out and touch the peaks, to breathe deeper of the wind.

"This is mine," he whispered. "This is my country. God help me to serve it well."

CHAPTER TWELVE

Tony looked gravely at Judge Brown sitting behind
the bench, then to the jury.

He chose his words carefully.

"Alaska has changed," he said. "In some ways for the
better, in some ways for worse. Thirteen years ago there
were sixty thousand people jammed into fewer coastal
areas than the fingers on one of your hands. Valdez had
ten times the population it has today. All but a few of
those sixty thousand are gone." He looked carefully at
the jury, most of them merchants from the town.
"Charley is one of the old-timers, so is the Judge, and I
like to include myself among them. A great many people
living in this town today have no idea whatever of the
life a prospector lives out on the creeks and the rivers
of the Interior. I'd like to show you." He turned dramatically to Judge Brown. "Your Honor, the cabin where
this alleged crime was committed is not too far from
Valdez. I ask that you adjourn this trial to that cabin in
order that the jury may understand more fully our de-

fendant's claim that he could not and did not commit this crime as charged."

Judge Brown blinked in astonishment. He beckoned the prosecutor and Tony to the bench. "What's the meaning of this, Tony? We can't pick up fifteen, twenty people and start sashaying all over the face of Alaska."

"Judge," Tony replied. "I have three dories with outboard motors tied up at the wharf. I even have lunches packed. I promise you," he said desperately, "we'll be back in five hours."

The young prosecutor looked suspiciously at Tony. "You're not asking the government to finance a picnic, are you? Who's paying for this?"

Tony rubbed his cheek ruefully. "I am."

"Well," said the Judge doubtfully, "I don't know. I've seen some odd things in the four months since I've been appointed, but this beats them all." He reached for his gavel. "No harm in sniffing a bit of fresh air." He looked hopefully out the window. "Rain's stopped. Might be a pretty good day at that." He banged on the desk with his gavel, "This court is adjourned to the Happy Day Mine on Gold Creek."

The long straggling procession moved out of the Courthouse and down Reservation Avenue to the dock. Tony good-naturedly shepherded the jury down to the float and into the three eighteen-foot dories that rose and fell on the heaving water.

The strange flotilla passed close by the abandoned wharf of the Valdez-Yukon Railroad, skirted the islands in the northeast corner of the bay, and chugged past the mud flats widening out around Mineral Creek. Four miles beyond, Tony turned his lead dory into the beach where Gold Creek came down from its starting point in the mountains high up by Shoup Glacier. The rain had stopped, but a high curtain of dark, threatening clouds hung over the entire expanse.

They pulled the dories high on the beach above the twelve-foot tides, then started on foot up the steep road. They climbed to the rocky shelf jutting out from Gold Creek, doubling back and forth as they gained altitude and entered the narrow canyon of Gold Creek.

"Let's wait here just a moment, Tony," Judge Brown called. He was puffing and wiping his face with an enormous red bandana. "Might just as well enjoy the scenery while we're out here."

Valdez Bay was spread before them in a panoramic view that included the distant mountain still capped in shadowy pockets and with traces of snow from a winter long past. Great towering cliffs rose at the west end of the bay; a white finger of Anderson Glacier pointed dramatically down to the water.

Tony looked through the narrow opening in the cliffs, toward Prince William Sound, the Gulf of Alaska, and the entire world that was waiting beyond. For a moment he thought of his family back in New York from whom he had been separated for so long. But there was work to be done. He pulled his watch from his pocket and looked at the Judge.

"All right, all right, we'll get along," the Judge said good-naturedly. "A man has to look at scenery like this kind of slow—just too much to take all in one gulp."

They continued north through the canyon, the puffing jurors spread out in a long thin line. In a wide basin to one side of the creek, completely dominated by the

towering rock walls, they came to the tiny cabin occupied the previous winter by Charley Fleur and Scot
MacAndrews.

The jurors clustered around Tony. "There was eighty
feet of snow in that canyon we just went through," Tony
said, "all of last winter. These two men were prisoners."
He threw open the door dramatically and, head bowed
to clear the low ceiling, he walked over and touched a
match to the candle on the table. The jury crowded in
after him.

"By golly," one of them said, "hardly room for one
man to turn around in, let alone two."

"That's what I wanted you to see," Tony said quietly.
"Two men were prisoners in this cabin for almost three
months. When they wanted to get outside, they went out
through this hole in the roof. The snow had the door
blocked completely. I spent several winters like this,
gentlemen." He lowered his voice, looking carefully
from one juror to the other. "You've heard of cabin
fever. Picture yourself sitting across that table from
another man, day after day, week after week. The two
of you become so irritable that the slightest motion or
gesture becomes the cause of a violent quarrel. To be
very frank, it becomes possible to hate even a man you
treasure as your best friend. There is only one remedy
for cabin fever." He paused.

"Dang it, Dimond," one of the jurors demanded, "tell
us."

"Get away from each other. Even if it means going
out in the middle of a blizzard, or hitting the trail at
sixty below, you've got to get away." He looked over his
shoulder at Charley Fleur standing by the open door-

way. "And Charley tried. He knew what was building up between him and his partner. He knew the danger. He packed his gear and started out. It was impossible to get through that canyon we just passed." He beckoned to Charley.

"Wait a minute," the prosecuting lawyer called. "We have proof. . . ."

"Sit at the table, Charley," Tony said quietly. "Tell the jury what happened."

The old man looked into the guttering light of the candle. "Old Scot had been acting queer," he said. "Kept seeing men hiding in that corner over there," he said, pointing to a jumbled heap of blankets. "We'd been snapping at each other, sure. I didn't want to stay. I knew something bad was going to happen. But like Tony told you, I couldn't get past them snowdrifts. I came back into the cabin," he continued, his voice sinking to a whisper. "He must've been waiting for me. He had his knife ready and he came on. I kept begging him to stop, but he kept coming, the knife all set. So I shot him." He lowered his head into his hands.

There was a deep silence in the cabin. The foreman of the jury cleared his throat and looked at Judge Brown. "All right if us jurors go outside and take a poll?"

Judge Brown nodded. "Better hurry. Looks like a big storm coming up. We'll have to get back to Valdez."

In three minutes the jury was back inside the cabin. "We find the defendant, Charles Fleur, not guilty of the crime charged."

"Let's get going," Judge Brown called out.

Old Charley Fleur still remained seated at the table. Tony stood by him.

"Glad it turned out well, Charley."

The old man held out his hand. "This place looks a lot better'n McNeil Island prison, Tony. If you don't mind, I just won't make the trip back with you folks. Kind of peaceful here, and I want to sit a spell and be grateful."

Tony shook his hand, and hurried down the trail after the others.

There were no specialists among the lawyers of Alaska. Over the wooden doorstep of Donohoe and Dimond came a variety of legal cases that taxed the ingenuity of the two men. There were minor arguments over property lines in the city of Valdez, claims and counterclaims on the gold mines studded about the city, legal work for the fish canneries along the bay, damage suits when the steamer *Mariposa* rammed into the wharf and almost demolished it, and criminal cases of all kinds, from theft to murder.

"First thing you know it'll be snowing again, and we'll be fighting another winter," Tom Donohoe observed one October morning in 1913.

"Not much of a fight when all you have to do is slip on an overcoat and hike across the snowdrifts to the Courthouse," Tony rejoined. "Man, think how lucky we are compared with those fellows still out on the trail!" He peered through the window. "What's all the shouting about?"

Donohoe threw open the door. Down Reservation Avenue a weather-beaten prospector came racing on horseback. "GOLD!" he yelled. "GOLD! They've struck pay dirt over at Chisana! GOLD!"

Tony lifted his head sharply. He looked back at Donohoe. "Chisana!"

"You know where it is?"

"You bet I do. Over beyond McCarthy. On Bonanza Creek. Never been there, but. . . ."

"Where you going?"

"I don't know for sure," Tony yelled back. "Just want to get some of the details from that fellow! Lock up the office for me, will you?"

Far down the street Tony could see men with packs on their backs shuffling out onto the wagon trail that led past Copper Center into the Interior country. For a moment he paused, his mind whirling back to the time, six years before, when he had taken part in the stampede out by Klutina Lake.

"What is it, fellow?" he asked the man on horseback. "What's all the excitement?"

"Just like I say—they struck it rich on Bonanza Creek just beyond Chisana! Best show of pay dirt anybody's seen since they hit up in Ruby in 1907. Excuse me, I've got to see the Judge. There's men traveling a hundred, two hundred miles trying to record their claims. I been elected a committee of one to come in and ask the Judge to appoint a Commissioner. Sure in tarnation need one. That camp out there is wilder'n a hornet's nest!"

"Commissioner. You. . . ." But the man hurried off before Tony could complete the sentence. He was still standing on the steps when Judge Brown came out and beckoned to him.

"How's the leg, Tony?"

"Good as it'll ever be, I suppose. What's up?"

"You weren't planning on going anywhere, were you, Tony?"

"To be truthful, Judge, I was. I've been up in this

country nearly nine years, and every year I keep promising myself I'm going to take a trip back and see my folks. Seems to me this would be a good time."

Judge Brown stroked his chin thoughtfully. "Sure wish you'd consider postponing that visit."

Tony smiled ruefully. "Guess I should plan on getting my folks to come up here—then I'd be sure to see them. Is it about Chisana?"

The Judge nodded.

"Think you could stand a trip over the trail?"

"Guess so."

"The miners up at the new strike have petitioned me to appoint a United States Commissioner to handle the recording of mining claims. The job is yours if you want it."

Tony looked at Judge Brown. He touched his chin reflectively. "A lawyer could pick up a lot of experience in one of those mining camps, couldn't he?"

"Bet your bottom dollar. You're jailer, marshal, coroner, town clerk, recorder, counselor, probate judge, prosecutor and defense counsel all mixed up in one. You'll be the only representative of the authority of the United States of America within fifty miles. Best experience in the world, Tony. That's why I thought of you."

"How soon do you want me to leave?"

"Tonight. The *Mariposa* sails at five for Cordova. You can take the train up to McCarthy, then hit the trail. That'll give you a jump on the stampeders who are packing the wagon trail into Gulkana then backtracking down to Chisana."

"I'm on my way."

"Come into the office. I'll swear you in."

CHAPTER THIRTEEN

In November, 1913, the new United States Commissioner for the mining camp of Chisana limped along the Goat Trail. His injured leg still pained him, and he smiled ruefully when silent stampeders, like wolves on the scent of blood, passed him by without a backward glance. For nine days he continued inland, following the faint trail that led from one river to another, boring a pathway through the towering mountains and glaciers. He followed the Nizina, in a hidden and beautiful part of Alaska, for twenty miles until it met with the fast-freezing waters of the Chittisone River. Then his impatient stride brought him over the Chittisone Glacier and the well-named Goat Trail that carried him through the Chittisone and Skolai passes to the west end of Russell Glacier.

He was in the heart of the big game country, abounding with mountain goats, bear and moose.

He took an entire day to negotiate twelve dangerous miles directly across the barrier of Russell Glacier. Then the White River became his guide for a time until he turned north at Lime Creek. Several times he sighted herds of pure white goats on the narrow strip of land he traveled, land that was dominated on either side by sullen glaciers. For thirty more miles he stumbled over the rough surface of the newly frozen tundra, gritting his teeth with the pain that stormed from his injured leg.

In the dark gloom of a snow-threatened day he sighted Chisana, a collection of tents and rude shacks housing two thousand stampeders jammed along the banks of the frozen Bonanza Creek.

It was at that moment he stumbled over a corpse sprawled on the trail. Tony knelt and turned the body over. The man had been shot between the eyes.

He hurried into the camp and stopped at the first tent. A bearded giant was forcing his shovel into the rock-hard gravel, trying to add to the growing mound of dirt he had thrown to one side.

"Who's in charge here?" Tony demanded.

"Ain't nobody, I guess. Stand back, mister, or you're going to get a shovelful of muck in your lap."

"There's a man dead on the trail just outside the camp."

"Oh, him?" the shoveler said without stopping his efforts. "Must be Boston Ryan. Got itching with another feller's claim. Heard tell they might be shooting."

"I'm Tony Dimond, the new United States Commissioner. I'm deputizing you my assistant. Get some help. Bring that body in. I'll summon a coroner's jury."

"Why, you can't do. . . ." The bearded giant looked belligerently at the tall man standing before him. His voice trailed off. "You the new Commissioner? Well, that's a mite different. Merriman's my name. Yantz Merriman." He placed his shovel to one side. "I'll go out and get the stiff. Guess I can do my duty as well as the next man."

That night Tony sat as Coroner, accepted the verdict of an impromptu jury that the victim, Boston Ryan, had died by the hands of persons unknown. "You, Yantz," he said, "see to it that the body is buried."

"Commissioner, you can't do that!" Yantz complained. "Takes six days to dig a grave in this frozen ground. I got work to do. Can't we just cache him in a tree until next spring when the ground's soft?"

In the morning Tony bought a tent from a man who had broken his arm in a fall down the mountainside. The sullen, dispirited prospector was on his way out to Valdez and the States.

In addition to the tent, Tony bought the man's cot. He cajoled another miner into giving him the necessary parts to construct a stove—two oil drums and a length of pipe. From a third, who rushed up to record a claim, he exacted payment not in money, but in an assortment of rough-cut timber that speedily became tables and chairs. One smooth piece of lumber he placed aside until the hammering and sawing was finished. Then, with black crayon, he printed the sign:

A. J. DIMOND
UNITED STATES COMMISSIONER

He was the only representative of law and order within fifty miles.

For days he was almost a prisoner within the tent, working from early morning hours until he fell asleep, exhausted, late at night. Long queues of rough-clad men, their clothing still smeared with the frozen mud of the creek beds, lined up before his tent to have their claims recorded. A miner committed suicide, and Tony left his table long enough to preside as coroner, supervise the burial, then probate the crude will the man had scrawled on a sheet of manila paper.

The bulk of his time was spent over the crude table, pen in hand, trying to make legible entries with ink that refused to flow properly at the sub-zero temperatures. He was pulled from his cot each morning by the demands of eager miners who were sure that any missed moment from their claims would rob them of a fortune. He made entries while gnawing hungrily on strips of cold bacon. He recorded documents while jiggling about from one foot to the other trying to ignore the intense cold that seeped through the dirt floor of the tent. He held court during storms that drove the men from their diggings but did not prevent them from jamming into the Commissioner's tent, loud in the accusations of wrongdoing one against the other.

He stood upright, his head brushing against the wet canvas warmed by the dull midday sun, and sentenced a sorry-looking individual to ten months in jail for stealing supplies from a neighboring tent. "You get on down to the jail, Jed," he said kindly, "and maybe we'll find a doctor to do something for that cold of yours."

The claims presented for recording were in a terrible state of confusion. In a great many cases, the boundary lines of neighbors overlapped, causing continual friction, arguments, and occasional bloodshed. In other instances, where lines did not meet exactly, "free spaces" occurred. These were leaped upon eagerly, with lone miners squatting on ten-foot frontages, guns clutched in hand, determined not to be ousted from the minute claims.

It was the Commissioner's job to untangle all the arguments and bring order from chaos. While miners labored to bore deep into the flinty ground, Tony wrestled with pen and ink, taking sworn statements from red-faced miners, making quick decisions that were accepted with elation by some, with dejection by others.

"One thing I got to say, Dimond," a disgruntled miner said when Tony had decided against him, "you sure bend over backwards to be fair. Anybody else but you handling this case I'd have shot that ornery skunk over there." He glared at the victorious plaintiff in the dispute.

"I've been through this myself, Tom. I know what you're up against. I try to remember my own experience when I make these decisions."

"Guess we're lucky at that."

All through the snow and cold sleet of the winter Tony remained within the ice-sheeted canvas walls of his tent, struggling heroically to untangle the ever-growing mound of paper work. Not until the first faint indications of spring late in April, was he able to get out on the frozen Bonanza Creek.

Yantz Merriman looked up briefly as Tony walked down the narrow twisting creek bed. In spite of the bitterly cold weather, the giant was in his shirt sleeves, pulling with all his strength on a heavy bucket on a long rope that dropped deep into a shaft.

"See any signs?" Tony asked.

The big man shook his head. He picked up a fist-sized rock and heaved it dejectedly across the narrow span of ice that marked Bonanza Creek. "Not a thing. Sometimes I wonder if we all are crazy up here. Digging around like a bunch of gophers, spending half our lives down in a deep hole, scratching away—man, it's not right."

"Billy James hit it big on his claim. Maybe you'll do it too."

Yantz shrugged his shoulders. "Maybe." He hauled up on the bucket and dumped the frozen earth. "Nothing shows this time next week, me and my partner are pulling out."

Tony shook his head in sympathy and tramped onward. A miner, crusted from head to foot with frozen dirt, crawled out of a hole and shook himself like a little dog coming into sunlight. He spied Tony and hobbled over stiffly. "Afternoon, Mr. Dimond. Glad to see you out in the open. Must've got writer's cramp recording all them there claims, eh?"

"Wasn't easy, Clance."

Clance Riley sidled up to Tony. He looked furtively over his shoulder before he spoke. "My partner, he pulled out yesterday. Quit. If you ain't got too much work as Commissioner, I'm offering you half a lay to come on with me."

Tony shook his head dubiously.

Clance tugged at his shoulders. "Come on, Mr. Dimond. You ain't got a thing to lose. Ain't but six hundred yards away around the bend in the creek that Charley Range hit. We could do it, too. Bedrock in another week maybe—and, man, we're rich!"

Tony shook his head firmly. He put his arm around

Clance's shoulder. "Sorry. I'm a lawyer. Nothing else. Just you keep digging. I'll help you celebrate when you hit."

He turned back to his tent. Before he ducked under the flap he looked far over the once bustling scene. Already an air of desolation had begun to invade the campsite that had been booming only three months previously. Abandoned tents were beginning to sag. Gone was the tense, electric atmosphere that had prevailed in the first days when he had come to Chisana as Commissioner.

That night, warming his fingers over a kerosene lamp, Tony wrote a letter to Dorothea Miller. "I'm afraid I've seen another assault on Alaska, and another defeat for the men who tried to conquer the country. The Chisana boom is finished. My job here will soon be over."

But the unflagging optimism that held most of the miners, who were sure the next panful of dirt would be the key to riches, kept the majority of the stampeders on the creeks surrounding Chisana through the month of May and deep into June.

The final blow came when a man who had come over the trail from Gulkana squatted by a roaring stove and announced casually, "A dozen surveying parties have been landed by Ship Creek over on Cook Inlet."

"What for?"

"Railroad. Ain't you fellows heard? The United States Government's building us a railroad from Seward right on up to Fairbanks. In a couple of years you won't have to walk to get into any strikes up in the Interior. Man, you'll just set back in them green seats and ride in. I'm heading over to the Cook Inlet country. There's going to be a lot of jobs at good pay waiting for guys like us."

As quickly as it had started, the Chisana boom was ended. Men disappeared from the outlying creeks, and then vanished in droves from the little tent communities that had dotted the entire length of the creek.

The few men who had made the original discovery still clung to their claims, certain that the next day would bring a return of the fabulous riches that had first started the stampede.

But Tony's work was finished. On July 1, 1914, he ended his term as United States Commissioner.

CHAPTER FOURTEEN

Late in the fall of 1914 Tony Dimond stood in the doorway of Lemon's Bakery in Anchorage, munching reflectively on a ham sandwich. On one side of Fourth Avenue a few wooden-fronted buildings reminded him of the frontier towns of the West he had seen when coming across the United States nearly ten years before. Teams of horses pulled around the brush fires burning in the center of the dirt street. Tony slipped the remainder of the sandwich into his pocket and stepped into the street, limping slightly as he skirted the mud puddles. The false front of Lemon's Bakery was the most imposing of the twenty buildings comprising the new town. Its lesser neighbors were large tents with wooden sides built in a hasty rush to respectability. Real estate signs proclaimed lots for sale. The shouting harangue of an auctioneer was heard drifting from the flats on Knik Arm just below the townsite.

Tony side-stepped two horses that pulled furiously at a big wagon bogged down in the mud. He put his shoulder to the wheel, pushed with all his strength, and the wagon groaned free. "Hey, mister," Tony called to the driver who was tipping his derby hat in thanks, "where's the railroad they're building?"

"Ain't none, mister. Just surveying crews out this year. Thanks for the push!"

Tony turned toward the flats, picking his way carefully over the slippery trail. He looked about until he found the tent marked with the wooden sign: ALASKAN ENGINEERING COMMISSION. He saw a tousle-headed man bending over a drafting board.

"I'm looking for Tom Riggs," Tony announced.

"You've found him. What can I do for you?"

"I'm Tony Dimond, lawyer for the Alaska Northern Railroad. They asked me to come over from Valdez and clear up a few questions on this sale to the government."

"Come in. Sit down." Riggs waved grandly to the wooden box by his drafting table.

It was mid-morning before the business discussion was concluded. The Alaska Northern Railroad, seventy miles of standard gauge track stretching from Seward to Turnagain Arm on Cook Inlet, was being absorbed by the United States Government which planned to build a railroad into the Interior of Alaska.

"I've been sticking pretty close to the Copper River country for the past eight years," Tony confessed. "Tell me about this railroad you're building."

"Easier to tell you about a trip to the moon," Riggs said in a moment of discouragement. He beckoned Tony closer to the topographical map of Alaska spread on his drafting board. His pencil touched the blue areas marking the Pacific Ocean. "We've already got your Alaska Northern Railroad stretching from an ice-free port, that's

Seward, up here to Turnagain Arm, about fives miles from where we're standing. What we plan to do," he laid heavy emphasis on the word, *plan*, "is to shove a line along the Matanuska River, then the Susitna River, break through Broad Pass crossing the mountains, and then slide across the tundra into Fairbanks."

"On paper," Tony commented, "it doesn't look too difficult."

"No," Riggs replied frankly, "it isn't. We'll have to pull some tricks along the Matanuska River to keep the track from sliding into the drink, and getting through the Nenana Canyon further north will be a real headache." He shrugged his shoulders. "But that's nothing compared with the trouble Mike Heney had when he planned the White Pass and Yukon Railroad—or when he was out in the field building the Copper River and Northwestern over in your country."

Tony measured the distance on the map with a pair of calipers. "Four hundred and seventy miles—two years should see it finished."

Riggs snorted in disgust. "Two years, my foot. Eight years would be closer."

"But, why?" Tony demanded. "It's no secret you're trying to open up the Matanuska coal fields. And carrying the line north to Fairbanks will open up the heart of Alaska for development. Why," he concluded excitedly, "this railroad could be the means of making Alaska a new state!"

Riggs nodded. "I know," he said sympathetically. "I've been in this country sixteen years. I was scrambling over the Saint Elias Range with the American-Canadian Boundary Commission when most other fellows were

ripping the creeks to pieces looking for gold. Some people, like yourself, know what this Territory needs before
it can ever hope to achieve greatness, can become a
home for people instead of a grab bag. But it's not
happening. Nothing's being handed to Alaska—we have
to fight for it."

"But why?" Tony persisted. "Why would anyone want
to slow the building of the railroad? There's a fortune in
coal waiting to be taken out of the ground. There's no
telling how many new placer and gold mines will be
uncovered if we can only get men and material into the
Interior."

Riggs nodded. "I've been saying the same thing for
years. Thought we had the problem licked when we got
permission to start surveying for the railroad." He
jammed his hands deep into his pockets and stood in
the doorway of the tent looking over to the leaden clouds
framing Mount Susitna. "We've had fourteen survey
crews out in the field all summer. Spent half a million
dollars—and now we've run out of money. Have to call
a halt until Congress appropriates some more funds."

"Can't they see how desperately the railroad is
needed?" Tony asked.

Riggs shrugged his shoulders. "We're a long way from
Washington. They forget. Mark my words," he said
earnestly, "it'll be eight years before you see a train
running clear through from Seward to Fairbanks."

"What can we do to hurry it up?" Tony asked quietly.

"We need somebody to get back to Washington and
say the right words, to tell Congress how valuable
Alaska is, how badly it needs railroads and highways.

It would take a good man." He looked quizzically at Tony. "Ever think of going into politics?"

Tony shook his head. "I've hardly got my feet on the ground as a lawyer, let alone becoming a politician."

Riggs nodded. Then he leaned forward. "I'm starting over the survey line tomorrow, making a final inspection before heading back to Washington with the other members of the Engineering Commission. Why not come along? I'll furnish horses, bedding, grub—everything." He rubbed his chin reflectively. "Don't mind admitting I'm looking for company. It's a mighty lonesome haul up into the country."

Tony shook his head doubtfully. "I'd never get back in time to catch the *Mariposa* over to Valdez."

"Take the stage down the Richardson Highway from Fairbanks right into Valdez. You'll see a part of Alaska you've never seen before."

Tony nodded. "You're on. When do we start?"

The next morning they struck out, following the line of wooden stakes from which red flags fluttered. This was the route of the unborn Alaska Railroad, snaking northward, following an age-old river highway that pierced the formidable Alaska Range of mountains.

For Tony it was a return to the wilderness, a plunge once more into the silent forests and quaking tundra that had been his home over in the Copper River Basin and north of the White River. This was a new Alaska, an unfolding of the curtain on still another section of the vast country that seemed to spread forever, from horizon to horizon. He listened attentively to Tom Riggs as their horses trod a field of yellow mustard. Beyond was the deep green of spruce and, farther yet, the blue and white of a glacier.

North of Anchorage along the Matanuska River, Riggs pointed to a fertile valley that would support hundreds of farmers. Beyond, he outlined the gigantic deposits of coal that showed outcroppings along the very line of the railroad stakes. Farther north, as they pushed onward in a steady rain, he showed how it would be possible, at long last, to bring in heavy mining machinery to recover gold from the wild glacial streams where hand placer development was no longer feasible.

Listening to him, Tony thought of Alaska as a sleeping giant waiting only for the coming of railroads and usable highways to spring to life as a powerful ally of the forty-eight states far to the south. "Everything is here," Riggs concluded. "What we need are people with vision to help us get it into the light of day."

Beyond the Alaska Range the two lonely horsemen followed the railroad stakes through the low hills that rolled down to the Tanana River. For the first time, Tony looked over the vast valley with its serpentine river twisting to the outer rim of the horizon. He pointed ahead and spoke to Tom Riggs. "It was nearly ten years ago I started out of Valdez, heading for this valley and the gold fields. Looks like I came in the back door."

At Fairbanks, where the line of survey stakes ended, Tony said good-by to his companion. Within four years, Tom Riggs was destined to become Governor of Alaska.

Tony climbed aboard a Model T Ford and braced himself for the grinding, bumping drive south along the rutted Richardson Highway, three hundred and sixty-four miles of dirt trail that was the only man-made link between the seacoast and the far Interior of Alaska. Bobby Sheldon, the driver, had been the first man to take an automobile across the dangerous highway the previous year. Three days later when Tony finally climbed, stiff-legged, from the battered car, he looked back toward the mountains over which the laboring auto had brought him. "Guess a man shouldn't complain," he said, rubbing his thigh tenderly. "When I first came up to this country nine years ago, it took the stage nine days to make the trip. If we keep cutting schedules like this—pretty soon we'll be flying!"

He patted the tin mudguard affectionately and limped down the plank sidewalk toward the office of Donohoe and Dimond.

Through all of 1915 Tony continued to add to his legal experience. His office, a small room nine by fifteen feet, was jammed with books and papers, a worn leather settee, bookcases, hatrack, and an old shelf filled with boots, leather jackets and raincoats. When the room was temporarily empty he leaned far back in his chair, cocked his feet on the desk, and clasped his hands behind his head. Then, in a loud tone, he and Tom Donohoe in the adjoining office talked to each other.

"If ever we can crawl from under this work load, Tom," he called, "I want to see more of the Territory."

"By yourself, or with company?" Tom's voice came booming back.

"What do you mean? Company?"

"Just thought you might be thinking of marrying Dorothea Miller. You sure got the ladies of Valdez making plans."

"Well, now," Tony drawled from his sanctuary in the

inner office, "you can just tell those fine ladies to forget their planning. Fact is, if they're over to the church about nine o'clock February tenth they might get to see a wedding."

Tom dropped his feet to the floor hurriedly, and raced around the partition. He thrust out his hand. "Well, by golly, you did it! There for a time I thought you were aiming to become the orneriest old bachelor in the Territory of Alaska! Congratulations!"

Late in November of 1916 Tony Dimond cradled his first child in his arms. He walked to the window and showed Marie Therese, wide-eyed and unblinking, the snow-covered mountains that seemed ready to topple upon the little town. "Welcome, pretty one," Tony whispered affectionately. "It took me twenty-four years to reach this country—and you came in on the wings of the morning! All your life you'll be proud to tell people that you were born under these mountains, here in Alaska."

The responsibilities of his new family caused Tony to increase his zealous practice of law. All day and long into the night, he pored over his books, preparing cases for court sessions. He became overworked, tired, and thin. His wife Dorothea worried about his health.

"You should take a vacation soon, Tony. All these years since you've been home to see your mother and father—it just doesn't seem right."

He nodded gravely. "I know. I want to go. But not yet. Not until the baby is stronger and you two can make the trip with me."

The next day at the office Tony opened a letter in the

morning mail and rushed around the partition to Donohoe. "Take a look at this."

Donohoe read the letter carefully:

Anthony J. Dimond, Esquire

*This is to notify you of your appointment as Special
Assistant District Attorney, Third Judicial District.
Please be ready to report aboard the Revenue Cutter
Thetis, two hours before the announced sailing time.*

F. M. Brown, Judge,
Third Judicial District,
Territory of Alaska

"Floating court trip out to the Aleutian Islands,"
Donohoe said enviously. "Wish I were going with you."
He rose to his feet. "I'll help you pack your books."

Three days later Tony's stomach had turned upside
down.

"You want to get better real fast?" a voice demanded.

The voice drifted down to Tony, plumbing the very
depths of his misery, then repeated hollow and insistent, "You want to get better?"

He raised himself upright. The deck of the Revenue
cutter *Thetis* slipped away and plunged downward into
the trough of waves bisecting the North Pacific Ocean.
He pried open his eyes, fighting the recurrent qualms of
sickness. He recognized young Johnny Kasavaroff with
whom he had become friendly on the first day of the
voyage. That was before the seas had started to roll in
mountainous waves, and his stomach had been nearly
normal.

For two days he had gone without food, living in a

twilight world where he was neither asleep nor awake. The old Revenue service vessel, its white bow lifting and falling as it followed an invisible line through the choppy green waters of the Gulf of Alaska to Kodiak Island, became a terrifying prison. Tony wished that he had wings so he could take off like a bird and fly back to his office in the old frame building in Valdez. There were still three thousand miles of green water waiting. And nothing could stop this journey.

Each year the sharp-nosed Revenue cutter picked its way from the harbor at Valdez, finding a passage down through Prince William Sound, then heading over to Kodiak. From there it set a course around the sharp dagger thrust of the Alaska Peninsula, stopping at the small town and canneries along salmon-crammed Bristol Bay. Finally it dropped down, island by island, along the weather-beaten Aleutian chain.

On board was Judge Brown, his secretary, the District Attorney, court reporters, deputy marshals, and clerks of the court. Tony Dimond, in his role as special assistant, was the lone defense lawyer.

Distances were great in Alaska. The cost of bringing an accused person, together with witnesses and deputy marshals, from remote villages to court headquarters was prohibitive.

The floating court solved the problems of distance. Instead of bringing the accused to justice, justice was brought to the accused.

Tony felt himself being lifted upright. Johnny Kasavaroff leaned over him. "You wait," he said.

Tony watched the sailor lash a thin line to a bucket. He saw him toss the bucket over the side and into the churning waters; then be pulled it upward. The young sailor stood over Tony, the bucket of sea water gripped in his hands.

"Drink," he said grimly.

Tony drank, choking and gasping on the vile-tasting salt water as it rushed down his raw throat. He held the bucket away, looking at Johnny accusingly. "I'm going to be sick," he croaked. "I'm going to be sick worse than before."

Johnny grinned. "That is right. But then you will be better. All better."

An hour later Tony pulled himself upright. The wind racing down from the Arctic struck him full and pleasantly on the brow. He opened the button on his shirt, breathing deeply of the fresh, rain-washed wind.

Suddenly the world stopped spinning, the pitching, heaving motion of the clumsy little ship no longer bothered him. His legs were strong; he could feel the strength coursing back into his arms, his wrists, his fingers. He lifted his face to the sky and smiled happily. He was no longer sick.

"Johnny!" he yelled, "I'm better!"

Tony Dimond was never again seasick. He remembered for the rest of his life the kindness of the little Russian-American boy who had tamed for him the turbulent waters of the North Pacific.

Day after day the *Thetis* crept westward into the setting sun, following the desolate Aleutian Islands. Treeless, some of them hardly bigger than the ship itself, while others were mighty stretches of mountain crowned by smoking volcanoes, these islands were the home for less than four hundred Aleuts, survivors of the early Russian occupation.

The little ship crept into harbor, dropped anchor and swung slowly to rest under the protection of bare, wind-swept mountains. Coarse yellow-brown grasses covered the slopes.

"Doesn't spring ever come to the Aleutians?" Tony asked Johnny while the sailor coiled a hempen line.

Johnny shook his head dolefully. "Even in July and August, I have seen snow swirling between the rain squalls." He pointed aloft. "Cold winds come from the North Pole, hit warm winds flowing over with the Japan Current through these islands." He made a sweeping motion with his hands then smacked them together. "When they hit—rain, storms, williwaws. A bad storm born in this region," he continued, "will move down the Pacific Coast, through Washington, Oregon, California —all over the United States."

"Tony!" Judge Brown called. "Let's get along. Boat's waiting to take us ashore."

The routine rarely varied. Arriving at a village, the party went ashore and set up court in any convenient building. Sometimes justice was dispensed in a cannery, in a private house, or in the back of a general store. But Judge Brown preferred schoolhouses. The children were given a holiday, and the teacher's desk became a rostrum. The jury, the lawyers, the accused and the witnesses fell naturally into the evenly spaced rows of desks.

By Tony's side was the accused, generally some fright-ened native who had committed an act of violence dur-ing a drinking spell. Tony noted that most of the cases brought before the floating court where caused in some way or another by the use of intoxicating liquors by the natives. He noted, too, with satisfaction, that Judge Brown tried to be extremely lenient with the bewildered natives, blaming not only the accused, but those who had provided the liquor. When it was possible, he excused the native with a warning. When it was necessary to pass sentence, the native was led back to the dory, carried out to the *Thetis,* and placed in the brig for the long journey back to the jails on the mainland.

Tony was saddened by the sight of these strangely quiet people who stood in such respectful silence before the court.

Their language remotely resembled that of nearby Eskimo tribes, and they were thought by some scientists to be of Eskimo origin; yet they lived in a world apart, content with life in almost unending rain and fog.

Tony remembered from his reading of Alaskan history that these Aleuts, when first discovered by Vitus Bering back in 1741, had numbered nearly 25,000—more than all the Indians living at one time in the Ohio Valley or in New England and New York State. They had lived in an abundance of animal life; their wants were simple and amply supplied. They had been peaceful, harmless.

Then the Russians came, and the poorly armed Aleuts tried to keep out the invaders. Their lances and bows were pitifully inadequate against Russian muskets and cannon. In one epic scene of cruelty, a Russian governor deliberately ordered the death of 3,000 Aleuts. The subdued natives accepted a condition almost like slavery. Their captors subjected them to inhuman cruelties, used them as animals, and exposed them to hardships that resulted in quick death. By the time Tony Dimond first saw them in 1917, the original 25,000 had dwindled to 2,000 or 3,000, and were too widely scattered in the far-flung islands to make an accurate census possible.

Tony brought all his skill to bear in trying to obtain an acquittal or a most lenient sentence. After one session, Judge Brown sought him out and placed his arm about Tony's shoulder. "I want to thank you for doing everything you could for that boy," the Judge said. "If you keep looking after the welfare of all Alaskans, as you have these Aleuts, you'll be doing a great service for the Territory." He paused and looked over the rail of the ship to the heaving waters. "We're starting home tomorrow. I think it's time you made another step in your career, Tony. The elections in Valdez will be held soon —why not run for Mayor?"

CHAPTER FIFTEEN

In 1920, when he was thirty-nine years old, Tony started on a political career that would eventually bring him the highest honors offered by the Territory of Alaska. It was his devotion to service for others that impelled him to become a candidate for Mayor of Valdez. The position was a thankless one, with no pay attached. It could be filled only by a man endowed with a deep sense of public spirit and community service.

Valdez, in 1920, was symbolic of the entire Territory of Alaska. It was a town of disillusionment. Eighteen years previously it had been an exciting city, almost a metropolis in the wilderness, the focal point for ten thousand men who used it as a springboard to reach the gold fields. The get-rich-quick promoters who swarmed around the mud streets during the period from 1902 to 1906 were loud in their prophecy of the glittering future awaiting the city on Prince William Sound. They spoke of the pay dirt that would be uncovered, the endless thousands of new settlers who would flood north and make Valdez, and all of Alaska, a new America. Yet even as they spoke their words had a hollow ring. The ships heading south to the states were even more crowded than those coming north. While the promoters tried frantically to stem the outbound tide of people, the glitter of Valdez gradually faded, the ten thousand became one thousand, and then, in a slow procession of years, ebbed further and further away, until scarcely five hundred people remained in the struggling city.

The people had come in a flood; they dribbled away in sad, bitter segments, cursing the land that had taken their time and their money.

Only the barest handful remained of the original gold seekers. They elected Tony Dimond mayor of the city.

In ten minutes he could walk from one end of Valdez to the other. In twenty minutes he could stride out the Richardson Highway and be in virgin wilderness. Looming overhead, day and night, month after month, were the only unchanging symbols of Alaska, the mighty Chugach Mountains.

He stood by the windows of his home, looking over the waters of Resurrection Bay. Dorothea came up behind him. "You're thinking of leaving Alaska, aren't you, Tony?"

He put his arm around her and shook his head. "Most of the times you can read my mind like an open book, but this time, Dorothea, you're wrong. I've told you before. I'm never going to leave the Territory. I don't care if everyone else leaves, if you and I and the children wander around these streets, caretakers for a ghost town, I'm never going to leave. I love this country. I want to be buried here."

And, so, filled with a devotion and love for Alaska that

only a few others possessed, Tony Dimond plunged wholeheartedly into the task of keeping intact a city that seemed determined to lose itself in the obscurity that was overtaking Alaska. He was down at the steamship wharf twice each week in the summer and every ten days in the winter to welcome both the disgruntled tourists who came in the rain, and the marveling tourists who came in bright sunshine, looking up to the massive mountains before they clambered aboard busses for the long, jolting trip up to Fairbanks. He encouraged the nebulous trucking companies that came to life briefly, competing for the freight hauls from the steamship piers to the dwindling mining camps in the Interior.

But even as a few secured footholds, the news came of the imminent opening of the Alaska Railroad, and Valdez was threatened again to lose its lone distinction: "Terminus of the only highway leading from salt water to the gold mining country of the Interior." When the few businessmen of the town spoke bitterly of the competition from the government-owned, tax-free railroad, Tony counseled patience. "We've got to think not only of ourselves, but of the entire Territory of Alaska. The railroad is good. Alaska needs it desperately."

"Yes, and when it's opened up, we won't get the tourist trade across the Richardson Highway."

Tony nodded soberly, but still he repeated, "We must think about the good of the entire country."

There were many times when he was discouraged, yet one thought was paramount. He had thrown his lot in with Alaska, and he would not desert the country. He had ample opportunity.

Early in 1921, with his wife and Marie Therese, who

was nearly five years old, and John Henry, who was barely two, Tony went south to Seattle and boarded the train to New York State for his first visit home in fifteen years. There was a tearful reunion with his elderly father and with his mother who was gravely ill. His brothers and sisters urged Tony to stay and make his home in New York State. But Tony, with his mother recovered, shook his head. "I'll come visit more often," he said, "but I have only one home—Alaska."

"Tony," one of his brothers urged, "be sensible. That country's withering on the vine up there. We've owned that Territory more than fifty years, and I'll swear it's worse off now than when we bought it from the Russians."

Tony studied his hands before replying. "I'm not saying that what you're saying isn't true. Alaska has been hurt. It's slipped badly. But it's not going to be that way always. There are some of us up there who intend to do something about it."

So the little family turned about again, and went aboard the steamer *Yukon,* and walked ashore to the snow-harried streets of Valdez. Tony sat with his City Council, planning new streets, new schools, new sewer systems, all the small, infinitesimal items that go to make a town or a city a better place to live in.

Yet gradually he came to understand that if Alaska was to be helped, he must do it on a scale wider than was possible while he acted as Mayor of Valdez.

His ten years of practice in law had earned him a host of friends; already his name had become a synonym for integrity. As he strode about the little town fighting for survival under the shadows of the glaciers, many people likened Tony Dimond to a gangling Lincoln striding the icy plank sidewalks and fording the deep paths on the snow-blocked streets. His name was entered as a candidate for election to the Alaska Territorial Senate, and he won.

He continued to serve as Mayor of Valdez, but he was embarked on a wider political field when he left with Dorothea and the three children—for Ann Lillian had been born on their return from the visit to his folks in New York State—and journeyed across the stormy Gulf of Alaska to take part in the excitement that marked the sessions of the Legislature in the old Territorial Building in Juneau, the capital city.

While Dorothea set up housekeeping in the small apartment they had rented overlooking Gold Creek Basin, Tony walked down to the mansion and paid his respects to Scott C. Bone, the tenth Governor of Alaska. Then he took his seat in the Senate chambers. There were only eight men representing all of Alaska. Across the hall sixteen representatives answered the roll call for House of Representatives.

The tumultuous sessions of the Legislature served as a training ground for Tony Dimond's later political efforts on a national scale. The sixteen representatives and eight senators were the voice of Alaska. The legislators, Tony among them, strove to fathom the causes for the lethargy that was hampering the growth of the immense Territory.

None of them pretended to be statesmen. Most of them, like Tony Dimond, had come to Alaska with a fierce determination to surge forward in the greatness they were sure was waiting the Territory. Most were lawyers with the same type of background that Tony possessed—years of prospecting and wandering over the land seeking gold that was even more elusive than fame. A few of them were destined to become extremely wealthy, as compared with most of their fellow Alaskans. Others were destined to have the sands of their lives run out before they saw more than a fleeting glimpse of greatness that would one day be Alaska's. All of them, without exception, shared a deep devotion for the land they loved.

The sessions of the Legislature were not quiet and sedate. They were wild and sometimes violent. In their eagerness to help the Territory to shake off the shackles that were binding the country, their voices rose in anger, fists were waved, blows were struck. To Tony, sitting in quiet astonishment, it seemed that the Alaska Territorial Legislature was engrossed, not in the advancement of the Territory, but in its own personal destruction.

Yet as he sat amidst the noises and tumult, he was able to analyze the situation. So vast was the Territory, so diverse the viewpoints expressed by the miners and lawyers and fishermen and operators of trading posts who comprised the Legislature, that it was impossible to get one clear voice to speak for Alaska. Each Legislator was concerned first with the welfare of his own District, and only later for the welfare of Alaska as a whole.

Late in the spring of 1923, Tony walked with Dorothea along the road that wound between Mount Roberts and Mount Juneau, the twin peaks that acted as a restraining wall holding back the immense glacier fields completely surrounding the capital city. The narrow dirt road clung to the side of Mount Roberts, hanging over the turbulent waters of Gold Creek where Joe Juneau had first discovered gold more than forty years before. Tony was thoughtful and his wife respected his silence. Hand in hand they walked deeper into the lush green growth of spruce and devil's club that crowded upon the narrowing trail.

"Sometimes, Dorothea," Tony confessed, "I wonder if we're all working for the good of Alaska, or for the good of four different Alaskas. Hunt and Aldrich can't seem to think of anything but what happens down here in the First Division. Brown and Ayer are all wrapped up in what's good for Nome and the rest of the Second Division. Snodgrass and Dunn act as though Fairbanks and Ruby were the whole of Alaska."

"And you and Senator Chamberlain?" Dorothea prodded gently.

Tony nodded his head ruefully. "I guess all we think of are Valdez and Seward and the rest of the Third Division." He helped Dorothea scramble over a log that blocked the trail leading up Mount Roberts. They climbed silently, saving their strength for the slow, steady upward haul that gradually brought them through thinning timber into the open land of shalelike rock above the timber line.

They settled down out of the wind, sheltered by a huge boulder. The panorama of Alaska stretched as far as they could see—white-tipped mountains, green covered islands, the pale green of Gastineau Channel and Stephens Passage three thousand feet below, and far across the peaks of Douglas Island a glimpse of the hazy blue expanse of the Pacific Ocean.

They sat in silence, looking over the land they loved.

"I'm thinking about the children," Dorothea finally said. "I hope they're safe with Mrs. Watkins. I told her what time to put Ann to bed." When there was no answer, she smiled and patted Tony's hand. "No need to ask you what you're thinking about."

"I wish I could speak for all of Alaska," he said.

"I know." Dorothea rose to her feet. "But wait until tomorrow in the Legislature. We've got to get back to the children."

The next day a clear voice echoed in the crowded Territorial chambers, pleading for unified action on the part of the Legislators, action that would bring help and recognition for the sorely tried Territory of Alaska. Gradually the clamor stilled, and eyes turned to the tall, lanky Senator from Valdez. He was respected by the men who sat about him, for many had shared his adventures on the Columbia Glacier, had explored with him the wild beauty of the Copper River country, had been with him on the stampedes that blazed new trails into the heartland of Alaska.

Speaking from the depths of his experience, and deeply moved by his sincere love for his adopted land, Tony Dimond became the rallying point for unified action on the part of the Alaskans in an effort to rescue the Territory from the indifference of its foster parents, the Congress of the United States.

The Legislators gathered in Juneau listened to his soft-spoken words. "We are caught between two forces," he said. "Men who steal our wealth while we quarrel, and men who are refusing us our rightful inheritance while they rule us blindly from four thousand miles away. We can no longer protect ourselves, thinking of this one as the Senator from Nome, or the Senator from Fairbanks, or the Senator from Juneau. We must speak now as the Senators from Alaska, representatives of a people who want to be free."

The cry for statehood was not new to the Territory, but never before had it been uttered with such great conviction and before a more attentive audience, and the Senators and the Representatives listened. From the beginning of American rule in 1867, Alaska had been a harried stepchild for distant politicians living in far-off Washington, D. C., men who were so taken up by the events in their own states that they were unmindful of the dark pall of lethargy that had fallen upon the northern Territory.

Sixty years after the purchase of the land from Russia, the Territory's plight was desperate. The riches of the sea were being depleted by outside interests who came in the late spring and left in the early fall, sending millions of cases of salmon to the grocery counters of the world, and giving nothing of real value to the Territory. Huge corporations were shipping mountains of copper away from the Territory, leaving nothing but gaping holes in the ground to remind Alaska of the wealth that had once been there. Other resources, like the vast stands of spruce and hemlock, were so tied up in Governmental regulations that the wood was left to rot on the stump rather than allow Alaskans to make use of it. So much of the Territory was given over to Government reservations that an Alaskan stepping from the confines of the seventeen towns walked abroad almost as though he were on foreign land. On the maps the area was marked Alaska; in reality it belonged to the Department of the Interior and was ruled from Washington, D. C.

"Let Alaskans decide what is best for Alaska!" This was the crusading cry of Tony Dimond. It was picked up and repeated over and over again with almost the same intensity of the early American colonists who first clamored for freedom from England, and with almost the same despair of success. For nine years the cry was echoed and re-echoed. Tony served in the Sixth and Seventh sessions of the Territorial Legislature, and again in the Ninth and the Tenth. The demand for greater freedom for Alaskans to conduct their own affairs was becoming more insistent. The people wanted a champion who would journey to Washington, D. C., to make known the needs of the Territory and the desire of Alaskans for the same freedom that had been given the forty-eight States in the Union.

In 1932, when he was fifty years old, Tony knelt in prayer in the living room of his Valdez home, gathered his three children for a last word, and kissed them goodby. Dorothea stuffed a wrapped sandwich into his pocket. "When I first saw you," she said, "you were hungry. I know that airplane won't be ten feet off the ground before you'll be hungry again."

"Not very dignified for a man who's campaigning for Delegate to Congress."

"If you'd waited for dignity, you'd never have had the courage to get off the boat twenty-seven years ago."

Tony campaigned vigorously for election as Alaska's sole Delegate to the Congress of the United States. His travels took him from Ketchikan, far to the south, to remote Point Barrow on the Arctic Sea. He spoke in

Anchorage and Fairbanks, in Juneau, Douglas and Sitka.
He flew in a small, five-seater plane over mountains,
forests, open water and endless tundra. He sought out
Alaskans on remote creeks and in new, thriving towns
like Anchorage. Early in September he wrote home to
Dorothea. "Tomorrow we're flying down to Iditarod.
We've been getting wonderful audiences. I've never
been so confident I was going to win."

When the small plane circled over the town of Iditarod,
Tony's thoughts were far away. He had been gone from
Valdez and his family for more than a month. Soon the
campaign would be over. Win or lose, he would be re-
united with his wife and the children.

The pilot brought the small plane on a glide down to
the Iditarod River. The floats touched and a huge sheet
of spray flew back over the plane. Gradually the speed
decreased and the plane, with its motor still roaring, its
propeller still spinning, eased gently toward the landing
pier. Tony leaped out as they came close, anxious to aid
the pilot in bringing the plane close to the wooden pilings
without harming the delicate pontoons.

He leaned forward. The propeller spun dangerously
close. The plane lurched and Tony fell forward into the
whirling blades.

CHAPTER SIXTEEN

When Tony's body disappeared under the water, the pilot stopped the motor, scrambled from the cockpit, inched his way out on the left pontoon, and dove overboard. When he reappeared, he had Tony under his arm. A rope was tossed out, and both were pulled ashore.

Blood was streaming from Tony's crushed shoulder. Hasty first-aid methods were applied, but the blood still flowed.

"Leave him peaceful," one old-timer said. "He'll be dead soon. No use getting him all riled up."

"Put a bandage on that shoulder," the pilot said. "I'm going to fly him into the hospital at Fairbanks."

Fairbanks was only 350 miles to the east, but the flight, in 1932, was not without its hazards even for the skilled bush pilots of the day. The float plane could set down safely on any straight stretch of water, but a mishap, a forced landing for refueling, could mean a delay of hours, days, even weeks. And with Tony Dimond near death, any delay at all in reaching Fairbanks would be fatal.

The plane took off, heading straight as an arrow for Fairbanks, ignoring the safe road of the rivers. Another passenger tended Tony's wounds, sending nothing but doleful reports to the pilot who sat forward. "Take it easy," the passenger pleaded. "This guy's going to be dead no matter what you do. Get back to the river so we'll know where we are."

But the pilot shook his head, and rammed the little ship forward. He became confused over the Tanana River, picked up the narrow waters of the Chena Slough, then beelined for the tall stacks of the Northern Commercial Company marking the town of Fairbanks. The pilot circled once around the town, pancaked down, and sat neatly on the Chena Slough, taxiing almost to the lawn of Saint Joseph's Hospital across the Slough from Fairbanks. Attendants were waiting to lift Tony from the plane and rush him to the operating room.

For a time it was believed that death was inevitable. The skin had been ripped from his back, and he had suffered a tremendous loss of blood during the wild flight from Iditarod to Fairbanks. His shoulder was broken in three places. Unlike his earlier misadventure on Young Creek, he did not have the tremendous strength of youth to help him rally quickly. It was only when Dorothea arrived at his bedside that his strength began to return.

A week passed, and Alaskans were assured Tony would live. A second and third week passed, and he was able to walk about the corridors of the hospital and look out the windows to the dark gray skies that heralded the coming of another early winter to Fairbanks. While he was still in the hospital, Alaskans went to the polls, almost a full month before the national elections down in the States. When the ballots had been counted, Anthony J. Dimond had been elected Alaska's sole delegate to the Congress of the United States. When he spoke now, he would be speaking for all of Alaska, directly to the men who controlled the fate of the northern Territory. Supported by Dorothea, he walked from the hospital with his shoulder and arm in a tremendous cast.

He rested for a few months at his home in Valdez, then with his wife and children, he started the long journey to the nation's capital. At Cordova, Juneau, Petersburg, and Ketchikan, anxious leaders came aboard the ship to speak to the tall, gaunt man who was going outside to speak for Alaska. "Get us back the Territory, Tony," they urged. "Get them to let us run our own lives!"

"I'll try," he promised.

The steamer carried them through the thousand islands of the Inside Passage, reversing the voyage Tony had taken twenty-seven years before. He stood on the deck of the ship, bundled up against the biting winter wind, pointing out to the children scenes that had been impressed on him so vividly when, frightened and almost penniless, he had slipped aboard the old *Excelsior.*

In the red-bricked station at Seattle, the Alaskan family boarded a train that turned south through California before pushing westward across Arizona and New Mexico into Texas. In New Orleans, where the family rested during the long journey, Tony walked with his children about the streets of the French Quarter, recalling episodes in that lonely, dispirited period of his life when he had been wandering almost aimlessly about the country. Then the five stepped aboard a Southern Railroad train that roared through the day and two nights to the capital city of Washington.

In the Union Station young John ran ahead and pulled back the door, and the little family that had traveled almost seven thousand miles from Valdez stood in awe at the sight that greeted them. Towering over the sagging buildings that blocked the view was the massive dome of the Capitol of the United States.

Tony cleared his throat. "Haven't been so scared since I fell in the Nizina River."

Dorothea squeezed his arm. "They can't yell any louder than some of those Legislators we knew up in Juneau."

"Dad," John Dimond said, "I don't think you're scared of anything. You just pretend."

Tony settled his family in the Rock Creek section of Washington, where the children could attend school conveniently. He went down to the House Office Building and was shown the offices he was to occupy for the next twelve years. With Dorothea and the children along, he joined a sight-seeing group that toured the House of Representatives and Senate Chambers. They walked silently through the lower floors of the White House during visiting hours with the flood of tourists that ebbed through the building. "Dad," young John whispered, "aren't you going up and see President Hoover?"

Tony shook his head. "Not until I'm asked, son."

As soon as President Franklin D. Roosevelt had been inaugurated the Seventy-third Congress swung into action. On March 9, 1933, Anthony J. Dimond took his seat in the House of Representatives, the voteless Delegate from Alaska. He had all the privileges of the other Congressmen, he could speak at length on any measure before the House—but he was not entitled to cast a vote. The men who sat all around him had absolute control over the destiny of far-off Alaska.

Tony Dimond was in the midst of history-making legislation during the dark days of the nation, during the awakening days when the country began to lift its head from the near-despair that had convulsed it, during the glorious days when the country suddenly became strong, vigorous and hopeful again.

One of Tony's first official acts was to introduce a bill calling for statehood for Alaska. He did not lose heart when the bill was completely ignored. Instead he turned his attention to other needs for the Territory.

"Build roads in Alaska," he pleaded when appropriation hearings were being held and funds for Alaska were being steadily whittled away. "Build roads or someday your sons will die in Alaska because an enemy will be shooting them down as they try to walk across impassable tundra."

Within ten years, his words of warning would have been fulfilled, but at the moment no action was taken. Alaska was four thousand miles to the west and north, and once again it was forgotten.

But the ex-schoolteacher who had explored the glacial streams of the Copper River Valley, the hunter who had come straight from the turbulent White River, the lean prospector who had washed his blistered feet in the sloughs of the Chitina River, continued his insistent prodding even though it seemed his voice was lost in the thunderous oratory that echoed about the House chamber.

Every two years without interruption, Alaskans returned Tony Dimond to Washington as their Delegate to Congress.

In 1935, six years before the disaster of Pearl Harbor, Tony stood before the House of Representatives and predicted that Japan would invade Alaska at the first opportunity. He had just returned from the fishing grounds at Bristol Bay where he had witnessed hordes of Japanese naval officers, thinly disguised as fishermen, who were openly sounding American waters and surveying Aleutian harbors for projected invasions.

One of the men who listened intently to the lean Delegate from the north was Brigadier General Billy Mitchell. The famous airman pointed to the maps Tony had spread before the Congressmen while he pleaded for defense bases in Alaska. "Japan is our dangerous enemy in the Pacific," Mitchell agreed. "They will come right here to Alaska," he thundered, ramming his fist against the map Tony had hung up. "The Territory is the most central place in the world for aircraft. I believe, in the future, he who holds Alaska will hold the world."

But the more Tony Dimond argued and pleaded for the defense of his beloved Alaska, the more his voice was unheeded by the Congressmen who controlled the appropriations.

A less determined man would have admitted defeat, but not Tony Dimond. He kept fighting, and the people of Alaska kept returning him to Washington to champion their cause. By 1939, after six years as a Delegate, his persistent hammering had made him a respected figure.

"Dimond of Alaska" was a man of respected stature among the famous in the halls of Congress.

But respect was not enough. The war in Europe was drawing closer, and yet not a single military establishment for national defense existed in Alaska. Tony was in Juneau on the 4th of July in 1939 when a detachment of soldiers came down from the military barracks at Haines. The seventeen men who marched in the parade represented almost the total armed strength of the United States in Alaska at that time.

When Tony returned to his home in the northwest section of Washington, D. C., he spoke to Dorothea of his fears for the safety of the Northland. "There's not a Navy ship anywhere in the entire North Pacific," he said. He walked to the window and looked out at the towering trees that marked nearby Rock Creek Park. "Every fisherman in Alaska has seen evidence of Japan's intentions. I've got to do something to wake up Congress. We've got to get military bases started up there."

And Congress, under the relentless prodding of the man from the Copper River, finally voted funds to start construction of airfields and naval bases in the northern Territory.

Almost from the time of his arrival in Washington, Tony had been urging the building of a highway from the United States, through Canada and into Alaska. Carefully he sketched routes for the road that would bring military help to Alaska should an enemy threaten the sea lanes in the north Pacific. But it was not until bombs had devastated Pearl Harbor that the War Department suddenly responded to the urgency of the message Tony had been repeating for years. He flew north to witness the start of one of the most dramatic construction feats in the history of the far north—the fifteen hundred miles of graveled road rammed through the wilderness of British Columbia and the Yukon Territory into the broad valley of the twisting Tanana River of Alaska. It was toward this river that Tony had been rushing years before when he joined the stampede to the Little Delta and almost lost his life.

He was back in Washington again and walking up the steps of the Capitol Building when an aide rushed to him with the news Tony had long been dreading to hear— the Japanese had bombed Dutch Harbor and invaded the two outermost Aleutian Islands, Kiska and Attu. For the first time in one hundred and thirty years an enemy had invaded American soil.

Tony bade his family good-by and flew north to the Territory. His plane carried him to bomb-scarred Dutch Harbor, and further west to the raw outposts that were being erected frantically in the Aleutians as a counter-measure to further Japanese encroachment. Watching the labor of Americans moving in the fog and snow to erect military barriers, Tony knew that upon their efforts rested the safety of Seattle and San Francisco and the entire West Coast of the United States.

With General George Marshall, Tony helped plan the network of military establishments that suddenly came to life in the Territory. At Fort Richardson, just beyond Anchorage, where he and Tom Riggs had urged their horses northward along the surveyed route of the Alaska Railroad, he saw the building of the greatest military camp in Alaska. In that camp alone were gathered soldiers in numbers greater than all the gold stampeders who once had swarmed upon the northland.

Tony made inspection trips out to Kodiak Island, to Adak and Amchitka, surveying the grim preparations that were being made on those bleak islands preparatory to throwing the enemy out of the captured Aleutian outposts. He was in Cold Harbor when the American convoy, crammed with combat troops, slipped out into the fog, and headed down the storm-battered chain of islands. Alone in a Quonset hut, he prayed for the success of the American forces when they landed at Massacre Bay on Attu Island, and inched forward through the mud and fog for their victory over the Japanese troops.

Whenever he could be spared from his legislative duties in Washington, Tony spent as much time as possible in this new Alaska, reborn with the wild surge of wartime activity. He bounced over the pitted dirt of the Alaska Highway, accompanying the troops and supplies that rolled in trucks over the new lifeline to the north. He sailed in ships crammed with troops that moved in twisting convoys through the waters of the Inside Passage. He flew high in the air in gigantic military planes that sped from Seattle to distant points in Alaska, covering in hours a vast sweep of Arctic space that once had taken him weeks to traverse on foot and on horseback.

In early 1945, when all danger to the Territory was past, and the successful end of the war was in sight, Tony was summoned to the White House. President Franklin D. Roosevelt, a long-time friend, and one who credited Tony with the successful efforts that resulted in the building of the Alaska Highway, shook his hand warmly.

"Some thirty years ago, Tony," the President said, "you went out to the Aleutian Islands with Judge Brown on the floating court."

"That's right, sir."

"I want you to go again. This time, as Federal Judge for the Third Judicial Division of Alaska. There's no one better fitted for the post."

Tony returned with Dorothea to Anchorage, the booming Alaska city where once he had stood in the mud of Fourth Street, looking in vain for the tracks of the new railroad. He took his seat behind the gleaming walnut bench of the courtroom in the concrete Federal Building. On his right was an American flag. Behind him, like a vast picture that would frame his entire life, was a massive mural of the mountains and glaciers of Alaska.

The kindness that had been a characteristic with him since his first days on the trail of Alaska still remained. As Judge for the Third Judicial Division, Territory of Alaska, he was respected for his wisdom. He enforced the law with firmness and charity.

Several times he went with the floating court back to the lonely Aleutian Islands. On Adak Island he climbed a low hill. All about him were the graves of soldiers and sailors and construction workers who had been buried in the black volcanic sand here on this hill rolling down to the Bering Sea.

In his long adventurous life, Tony had always been deeply religious. As was his habit, he prayed aloud. "These men," he said into the wind that raced endlessly over the bleak island, "died that all of Alaska, and all of America, might remain free. God grant that an enemy never again set foot on American soil."

He turned and walked far down to the waiting Coast Guard Cutter.

At the new International Airport in Anchorage, planes flew in from Seattle and Chicago, pausing for refueling before taking off for the Orient. Other planes sped north to Fairbanks in barely more than an hour, a journey that once had taken two to three weeks on the trail. The entire Territory was crisscrossed by networks of airlines that probed into every remote corner of Alaska. Fast diesel trains rumbled overnight from Anchorage north to Fairbanks, while mammoth truck tractors raced over the Richardson Highway north to the Interior of Alaska, and downward over the Alaska Highway to the States.

There was a continual influx of newcomers as Anchorage boomed to new heights of postwar prosperity, and the population doubled and doubled once again. The work load in the Federal Court became increasingly heavy. A petition was presented to the President to appoint another Judge to help Tony in the unending flow of cases that appeared in his court. But there was no help coming.

Tony's steps became slower as he walked the streets to the Courthouse each morning. Lifting his eyes he could see new "skyscrapers" on the very spot where he had once stood before Lemon's Bakery chewing on a sandwich. But the massive form of Mount Susitna in the distance was exactly as he had seen it nearly a lifetime before. There were a few external features of Alaska that were changing, but the land itself was still almost untouched.

In 1949 he was called suddenly from the courtroom.

He ran to the nearby Catholic Church where he found
the lifeless form of Dorothea. She had knelt quietly in
prayer and had died before the altar.

Now Tony plunged into the battle for Statehood with
even more vigor than before. His daughter Marie Therese
had entered a convent in Washington, D. C. His son
John was practicing law in Juneau, the capital city. The
youngest child, Ann Lillian, had married and was living
in Ketchikan, first city of Alaska.

When court was not in session, he gave himself over
entirely to his cherished dream, statehood for Alaska.
He returned several times to Washington, D. C., to testify
before Congressional committees, pleading the cause of
statehood. At times he was disheartened by the seeming
indifference of the new settlers in Alaska to this vital
need. Yet always he continued the battle. He neared his
fiftieth year in Alaska, and the goal was still not reached.
He prayed that he would live to see the day when Alaska
would be admitted as the forty-ninth State in the Union.

In the middle of April, 1953, when he was seventy-one
years old, he made a fourth trip to Washington to testify
before a Congressional Committee considering a new
version of the Statehood Bill. He knew his strength was
failing. He told friends that he paced the floor, debating
whether it might not be better simply to send a telegram
expressing his views. "However," he concluded, "this is
no time for us who believe in Statehood to sit back."

He walked through the streets of Washington. Quietly
he slipped into the House of Representatives when the
chamber was empty, sitting in the chair he had occupied
for twelve years, listening to the dim echoes of the his-
toric speeches he had once heard reverberating through

the high-ceilinged room. At the committee hearing his keen, expert analysis of the benefits to be derived from statehood for Alaska had a great effect on the listening Congressmen, but once more the cause was lost.

Tony returned to Anchorage. For five more weeks he presided in the courtroom, instructing juries, admonishing prisoners. On the twenty-first day of May, 1953, he suffered a heart attack. One week later, on May 28, 1953, he died at Providence Hospital in Anchorage.

TERRITORY OF ALASKA
OFFICE OF THE AUDITOR
JUNEAU, ALASKA

AN ACT
DESIGNATING NOVEMBER 30TH AS ANTHONY J. DIMOND DAY

(S.B. 141)

Be it Enacted by the Legislature of the Territory of Alaska:

Section 1. It is the intent of this act to honor the memory of Anthony J. (Tony) Dimond by giving official recognition to the great debt of gratitude owed by Alaskans to a great humanitarian and servant of and for Alaska, evidenced by the following facts and events:

(a) He came to Alaska at the age of 23 years to become a prospector in the Valdez area but shortly thereafter turned to the practice of law.

(b) Beginning in 1913 he was actively connected with the practice of law in Alaska for forty years. He was U. S. Commissioner at Chisana in 1913, and special assistant to the United States Attorney at Valdez in 1917.

(c) His devotion to the public service is witnessed by the fact that he served as a member of the Alaska Territorial Senate in the sessions of 1923, 1925, 1929 and 1931; and that he was Mayor of Valdez for nine years and Delegate from Alaska to the Congress of the United States from 1933 to 1945; and that from 1945 to the time of his death on the 28th day of May 1953 he was a judge of the District Court of Alaska.

(d) As a judge "Tony" Dimond was a protector of human rights particularly of the rights of those accused of crime who came before him during his tenure on the bench in Alaska.

(e) As Delegate from Alaska he warned the Congress to fortify Alaska and had his warnings been heeded the Japanese attack might never have taken place and the great cost of defense in Alaska would have been much less through following his prudent foresight.

(f) A "Christian gentleman," Judge Dimond was a firm believer in the natural law which existed according to his philosophy always before governments or written laws of man's making, and which was to be regarded as the highest law controlling mortal men.

(g) As a lawyer, legislator and jurist he labored well and diligently for the cause of statehood for Alaska and was an ardent and eloquent advocate and supporter of that cause to which his devotion was dedicated.

(h) His legal ability and qualities as a judge were of the highest type; and his quiet manner and unfailing courtesy to witnesses and counsel who came before him gave clear evidence of his vast knowledge of human nature and its frailties.

(i) A personification of a merciful but impartial judge, he at all times maintained that tranquility of order and spirit which is so rare in the affairs of men; yet he gave unstintingly of his time and ability in public and civic affairs.

(j) Few men in Alaska have ever been called upon to serve their country in such high offices and for such extended periods of time, and none has served with more conscientious fidelity.

Section 2. November 30th of each year is hereby designated Anthony J. Dimond Day in honor of "Tony" Dimond, said day to be observed by appropriate school assemblies and programs, and other suitable observances and exercises by civic groups and the public at large.

BIBLIOGRAPHY

Suggestions for further reading about Alaska

Allen, A. A. (Scotty). *Gold, Men and Dogs,* G. P. Putnam's Sons, New York, 1931.

Curwood, James Oliver. *The Alaskan,* Cosmopolitan Book Co., New York, 1923.

Darling, Esther B. *Baldy of Nome,* A. M. Robertson, San Francisco, California, 1913.

Davis, Mary Lee. *Uncle Sam's Attic,* W. A. Wilde Co., Boston, Mass., 1930.

Harrington, Rebie. *Cinderella Takes a Holiday in the Northland,* Fleming H. Revell Co., New York, 1937.

Herron, Edward A. *Alaska: Land of Tomorrow,* McGraw-Hill Book Co., New York, 1947.
The Return of the Alaskan, E. P. Dutton and Co., New York, 1955.

Hubbard, B. R. *Cradle of the Storm, Dodd,* Mead & Co., New York, 1936.
Mush, You Malemutes, America Press, New York, 1932.

London, Jack. *The Call of the Wild,* The Macmillan Co., 1903.

McGuire, James A. *In the Alaska-Yukon Game Land,* Stewart & Kidd, Cincinnati, Ohio, 1921.

INDEX